D1243187

The Muslim and Christian Calendars

Dinumerare nos doce dies nostros, ut perveniamus sapientiam cordis.

PSALM 89, 13 (New Latin Version).

O teach us to number our days: that we may apply our hearts unto wisdom.

The Muslim and
Christian Calendars

being tables for the conversion of
Muslim and Christian dates from the
Hijra to the year A.D. 2000

G. S. P. FREEMAN-GRENVILLE

London
OXFORD UNIVERSITY PRESS
New York Toronto * 1963

Oxford University Press, Amen House, London E.C.4

GLASGOW NEW YORK TORONTO MELBOURNE WELLINGTON
BOMBAY CALCUTTA MADRAS KARACHI LAHORE DACCA
CAPE TOWN SALISBURY NAIROBI IBADAN ACCRA
KUALA LUMPUR HONG KONG

Printed in Great Britain by Western Printing Services Limited, Bristol

Introduction

At the twenty-fourth annual meeting of the East African Swahili Committee, held in Zanzibar in September 1960, I was told that the absence of any comprehensive work dealing with the Muslim and Christian Calendars was causing difficulties. The Committee had acquired a considerable number of historical documents and of dated collections of poetry; and members were experiencing difficulty in calculating the dates, years, months and days of the week, as given in the Muslim Calendar, to their Christian equivalents. Subsequent enquiries kindly made by the Secretary, J. W. T. Allen, showed that all the Courts in East Africa and in the Dominions of His Highness the Sultan of Zanzibar had difficulty in finding a precise Christian date from a Muslim one.

I first thought of Sir Wolseley Haig's *Comparative Tables of Muhammadan and Christian Dates*, which has long been out of print. It does not contain, however, any tables for ascertaining the days of the week. Moreover, close examination showed that it had very inadequate information on a number of material points, a considerable number of printer's errors and several inaccuracies. It gave no assistance to those who might wish, for reasons of government or business, to know when the Christian or Muslim festivals fall within one or the other Calendar.

It was therefore thought worth while to construct a completely new work to meet all the desiderata. A Muslim or a Christian can find in this work the equivalent of any date or day in either Calendar from the first day of the Hijra up to the Christian year A.D. 2000. Both can calculate from it the date of any future festival.

So far as Christian Movable Festivals are concerned, so called because they depend on the date of Easter as fixed by the lunar calendar, it has been thought sufficient to calculate them up to the year A.D. 1990. On the representation of Members of the British Parliament, it has been proposed to fix the date of Easter. This proposal was accepted by the late Supreme Pontiff, Pope Pius XII, as well as, for the Church of England, by the Archbishop of Canterbury. The matter is one of current international negotiation, and it is possible that the Christian Calendar will be changed within the present generation, and the date of Easter fixed. When this has been done, Table Eight will be out of date.

I must acknowledge the kindness of J. W. T. Allen for having read this work in draft and for having made a number of valuable suggestions.

Oxford, 15 August 1961   G.S.P.F./G.

Table of Contents

1 The Muslim Calendar

THE MOON REVOLVES ROUND THE EARTH IN $29\frac{1}{3}$ DAYS. BUT because the Earth is itself in motion, this revolution in fact takes approximately $29\frac{1}{2}$ days. The Earth itself performs a complete revolution once in twenty-four hours, and at the same time revolves round the Sun in slightly less than $365\frac{1}{4}$ days. It follows that a calendar based upon the Earth's movements round the Sun requires constant adjustment if it is to remain in relation to the seasons of the year, and that a calendar based upon the Moon's changes cannot, without adjustment, be brought into relation with it.

The ancient Semitic Calendars were based upon the movements of the Moon, and from them both the Christian and Muslim Calendars ultimately derive. They still both follow the same days of the week.

The ancient Arabian Calendar consisted of twelve lunar months. In each third year there was an additional, thirteenth, month, in an attempt to keep the lunar year in relation to the solar year and the agricultural seasons. This led, however, to considerable confusion, since in fact the resulting years corresponded neither with the solar nor with the lunar system.

The Muslim Calendar is a religious calendar, and based solely upon the Moon's changes. In the Mishkat, book XI, chapter XI, it is related that the Prophet Muhammad, reciting the khutbah, or Sermon, at his Farewell Pilgrimage, said: 'A year is twelve months, as at the time of Creation.' In the Quran, Sura IX, verse 36, it says: 'Verily twelve months is the number of the months with God, according to God's Book, ever since the day when He created Heaven and Earth.'

In A.D. 622 the Prophet Muhammad was invited by seventy-five inhabitants of Yathrib, now called Medina, to leave Mecca and to make his home with them. After a short delay, two hundred of his followers secretly left Mecca on his instructions. He followed them alone, departing from Mecca on 16 July A.D. 622, and arrived at Medina on 22 September A.D. 622. Seventeen years later the Caliph 'Umar found it necessary to regulate the calendar. He ordered that the lunar year of twelve months should be held to have begun on the day on which the Prophet Muhammad left Mecca, 16 July A.D. 622, and that the Muslim era should be counted from that date. The Prophet Muhammad's departure from Mecca is known in Arabic as the Hijra, or Migration, and the Muslim Calendar is thus known as the era of the Hijra. In English it is usually abbreviated in a Latin form: A.H., that is, Anno Hijrae. In this way 16 July 622 became officially 1 Muharram A.H. 1.

As has been said, the Muslim Year is a lunar year which takes no account of the solar year nor of the change of the seasons. Thus, in relation to the solar year, it recedes approximately eleven days each solar year, with the result that in each $32\frac{1}{2}$ years it passes through all the solar seasons. Thus, if in a given lunar year the fasting month of Ramadhan occurs during the heat of the summer, it will occur within the cool season $16\frac{1}{4}$ years later. It is to be noted that this retrogression of approximately eleven days each year cannot be regarded as precise: according to the actual time of the Moon's changes within the solar year, it is sometimes necessary to reckon it as a change of ten days and on other occasions as one of twelve days. It is because of these difficulties, and especially those of agriculturalists, that the East African Governments all officially use the Christian solar Calendar. This is also the case in many of the more westernized Muslim countries, in which both Muslim and Christian Calendars are in force at the same time. For the same reason the Swahili agriculturalists of Zanzibar and Pemba have continued to use their own ancient calendar, which is based partly upon the Sun's changes and partly upon the movements of the Pleiades and other stars.

Although in modern times mathematically calculated Muslim Calendars are printed and widely circulated, it must be emphasized that officially the beginning of each month, and most especially the beginning of the fasting month of Ramadhan, and its end with the first day of the following month Shawwal, depend upon the Moon's changes. Strictly speaking, the new month does not begin until the New Moon has been actually sighted. As to the beginning and end of Ramadhan, while the announcement can in theory be made by any reputable Muslim, the normal observance is that the announcement is made by a Qadi or by some other prominent member of the community. In many places the announcement is made by the firing of a gun, which also marks the opening and close of each day's fasting. The precept of the Quran (Sura II) is strictly observed: fasting begins when a white thread can be distinguished from a black thread at the dawn of the day.

It frequently happens that the sky is overclouded, and that there is doubt both as to the beginning and end of Ramadhan because the New Moon has not been seen. In this case, as to the beginning of Ramadhan, the normal rule is that Ramadhan is held to begin on the completion of thirty days from the beginning of the preceding month. There are, however, some places in which this rule is not observed. As to 1 Shawwal, on which the 'Id al-Fitr is celebrated, fasting cannot cease nor the festival begin until the New Moon has been actually seen. In these days of rapid communication this seldom causes real difficulty to the more modern spirits. Nevertheless, there are many who hold to the ancient traditions, and these are in a majority.

It thus follows that, while the following tables are calculated strictly within terms of the actual changes of the Moon, the results cannot be applied with the same strictness. Since the observation of the New Moon is necessary to begin each new month, where there has been cloudy weather, it is quite possible to find, as the writer himself has done, three adjacent villages each claiming a different date as correct, according to the day on which the New Moon had been sighted. It is necessary to make allowances for this in comparing documents, or in hearing evidence in the course of which the witness has given a date according to the Muslim Calendar.

Further difficulty can arise from the fact that the Muslim and the Christian day do not precisely correspond. Whereas the Christian day is reckoned from midnight to midnight, the Muslim day begins at sunset, time being usually reckoned in twelve-hourly periods from 6 p.m. to 6 a.m., and again from 6 a.m. to 6 p.m. Thus in correct Arabic, Swahili and a number of other languages, the Christian 7 p.m. is 1 o'clock in the evening, and so on. For this reason the days of the week are likewise reckoned by Muslims from sundown to sundown, and what to the Muslim is Sunday evening is to the Christian still Saturday evening, and so throughout the week. If these differences are overlooked, an incorrect interpretation can be put upon documents or upon oral evidence.

It is necessary to remark, however, that in many Arab cities subject to western influence the Christian clock and method of reckoning the days of the week is beginning to be used amongst the more sophisticated, and that those accustomed to the ancient Arabic method can find themselves confused. The latter method, however, still prevails amongst tribesmen and in the smaller towns, and universally throughout East Africa.

It is also necessary to note that in certain remote areas clocks are set daily to coincide with the actual local sunrise, a further source of confusion to those accustomed to western conventions.

3

2 The Christian Calendar

With certain important changes, the rules governing the present Christian Calendar are those established by the General Council of the Church held at Nicaea in A.D. 324. The years are reckoned from the Birth of Christ, and so are known as years A.D. (Anno Domini: in the year of the Lord). The Calendar follows the solar year of $365\frac{1}{4}$ days, each common year consisting of 365 days; and each fourth year, or Leap Year, making up the omitted quarters by containing 366 days. The additional day is intercalated on 24 February, the Feast of St. Mark which falls on that day being transferred to the following day, making the month of February consist of 29 days instead of 28 days as in a common year. This system, however, was not precisely in accordance with the solar year, since in fact the additional quarter day is not a complete quarter but only almost so. Thus, in the course of time, the Christian Calendar became in advance of the solar system and out of relation to the seasonal changes and to the agricultural year.

While recognizing the solar year for general purposes, the Council of Nicaea did not recognize it for some religious purposes. The Death of Christ on the Cross took place at the Jewish Passover, a festival fixed by the lunar Calendar. It was therefore ordered that the celebration of Good Friday and Easter should take place on the Friday and the Sunday nearest to the Full Moon on which the Passover fell, that is, the Paschal Full Moon. It is for that reason that the cycle of Christian Movable Festivals changes annually in relation to the date on which Easter has fallen. These dates are shown in Table Eight.

In the year A.D. 1582 it was realized that the Christian Calendar had reached ten days in advance of the solar year. Thus Pope Gregory XIII ordered that ten days in that year should be omitted from the month of October, and that the fourth day of that month should be followed immediately by the fifteenth day. And, in order to prevent the further accumulation of error, he also ordered that while each year divisible by four should contain 366 days as previously, centenary years whose first two figures are not divisible by four should not be Leap Years. Thus A.D. 1600 was a Leap Year, but not 1700, 1800 or 1900, while A.D. 2000 will be a Leap Year. In this way the Christian solar Calendar was once again brought into relation with the lunar Calendar in use for the computation of the date of Easter, which was once again restored to its primitive position as the Sunday nearest to the Full Moon following the Vernal Equinox.

The Christian Calendar as reformed by Pope Gregory XIII was accepted throughout Europe in 1582, except in England, Russia and Sweden. The unreformed Calendar is still followed in Russia for ecclesiastical purposes. The reformed Calendar was not adopted in England until 1752, and special information is included in Tables One and Five to enable the conversion of Muslim dates to both the unreformed and the reformed Calendar between 1582 and 1752. The reformed Calendar is spoken of as the Gregorian, or New, Style; and the unreformed Calendar as the Julian, or Old, Style.

3 Method of Using Tables One to Eight

TABLES ONE TO EIGHT ENABLE THE CONVERSION OF ANY given Muslim date to the corresponding Christian date, or vice versa, including also the days of the week and the principal festivals of either religion. These tables contain the following information:

Table One has four columns, and a fifth column between the years 1583 and 1752 added in brackets. The first column shows the Hijra Year; the second column the Christian date of 1 Muharram, on which the Hijra Year begins; the third column the number of days which have already elapsed in the Christian Year before that day; and the fourth column the day of the week on which that Christian Year began. The fifth column between the years 1583 and 1752 shows the day of the week on which the unreformed Christian Year began, as observed during that period in England, Sweden and Russia.

Table Two shows the Muslim months, the first column being the day of the month, and the second the day of the Hijra Year.

Table Three shows the months of the Christian Year: the first column shows the day of the year in both common and Leap Years, the second column the day of the month in common years, and the third column the day of the month in Leap Years. It will be observed that the days of the year as between common and Leap Years differ only after 28 February.

Table Four shows the days of the week in the Christian Year arranged as a perpetual calendar according to the day of the week on which that year has begun, for both common years and Leap Years, as shown in columns four and five of Table One.

Table Five is a separate calendar for the last three months of the year A.D. 1582.

Table Six is a list of the Principal Muslim Festivals.

Table Seven shows the Principal Fixed Christian Festivals which are determined by the solar calendar.

Table Eight shows the Movable Christian Festivals between the years A.D. 1960 and 1990 as determined by the changes of the date of Easter.

6

There now follow the six differing methods by which Muslim dates are converted to Christian dates, the method of finding a Muslim date from a Christian date, and the method of employment of the tables for the various festivals. Those using these tables are recommended first to look at the words italicized which describe each different method, and to make sure that the correct method is being employed.

i. *To find a Christian date from a Muslim date.*

Supposing the reader wishes to find the Christian date corresponding to
7 Muharram 1040, he should first take a piece of paper and write this date
in full at the top. He should then turn to *Table One*, where he will find
that the Hijra Year 1040 began on 10 August A.D. 1630, on which day
221 days of the Christian Year had already elapsed. He will also note that
the year A.D. 1630 began on a Sunday. Underneath the Muslim date he
should therefore write: A.H. 1040 began 10 August A.D. 1630 (Sunday)=
221. He should next turn to *Table Two*, where it shows that 7 Muharram
is the 7th day of the Muslim Year. Thus, underneath the second line of
what he has written, he puts: 7 Muharram=7, being careful to ensure that
the figure 7 falls below 221 in the preceding line. He then adds 221+7,
the result being 228. He should then look for the 228th day of the Christian Year in *Table Three*, which shows it to be 16 August. Finally he
turns to *Table Four*, bearing in mind that A.D. 1630 was a common year
which began on a Sunday. Thus he finds that 7 Muharram A.H. 1040
began at sunset on Wednesday, 16 August 1630. The results of his work-
ings will appear as follows:

    7 Muharram 1040
    A.H. 1040 began 10 Aug. A.D. 1630 (Sunday)=221
    7 Muharram   = 7
                                          ─────
                                       228=16 Aug. 1630,
    Another example: Wednesday.
    16 Jumada al-Aula 1323
    A.H. 1323 began 8 March A.D. 1905 (Sunday) = 66
    13 Jumada al-Aula   =134
                                               ─────
                                            200=19 July 1905,
                                                Wednesday.

ii. *To find a Christian date from a Muslim date where the Christian Year is a Leap Year.*

All Leap Years are distinguished in *Table One* by the sign * immediately preceding the Christian date corresponding to 1 Muharram. In this case the reader must refer to the third column of *Table Three* when ascertaining the Christian date, and, in using *Table Four*, to use one of the calendars for a Leap Year.

For example:

27 Safar 1351
A.H. 1351 began * 7 May A.D. 1932 (Friday)=127
27 Safar   = 57
                                    ─────
                                    184=2 July 1932,
                                            Saturday.

B   9

iii. *To find a Christian date from a Muslim date where the Hijra Year begins in one Christian Year but the Muslim date is in the following Christian Year.*

Most Hijra Years begin in one Christian Year and end in the following Christian Year. If the Muslim date to be converted occurs in the second of the two Christian Years, it is necessary to deduct 365, being the number of days in a common year, from the sum of the days elapsed in the Christian Year and the number of days reached in the Hijra Year. For example:

2 Shawwal 904
A.H. 904 began 19 Aug. A.D. 1498 (Monday)=230
2 Shawwal   =268
                                     ————
                                   498
Deduct the number of days in A.D. 1498:   365
                                   ————
                             133=13 May 1499,
                                       Monday.

In this case care must be taken to ascertain the day on which A.D. 1499 began, consulting *Table Four* accordingly.

Another example:

12 Dhu al-Hijja 1366
A.H. 1366 began 25 Nov. A.D. 1946 (Tuesday)=328
12 Dhu al-Hijja   =337
                                   ————
                                   665
Deduct the number of days in A.D. 1946:   365
                                   ————
                             300=27 Oct. 1947,
                                       Monday.

iv. *As iii, but when the first of the two Christian Years is a Leap Year.*

In this case it is necessary to deduct 366 days, and not 365, and to use the calendars appropriate to Leap Years in *Table Four*.

For example:

21 Ramadhan 630
A.H. 630 began * 18 Oct. A.D. 1232 (Thursday)=291
21 Ramadhan   =257
                                          ———
                                          548
                                        —366
                                          ———
                                          182=1 July 1233,
                                                Thursday.

v. *As iii, but when the second of the two Christian Years is a Leap Year.*

In this case it is necessary to deduct only 365 days, but the third column of *Table Three* must be used to ascertain the Christian date and also the calendars appropriate to Leap Years in *Table Four*.

For example:

1 Shawwal 1202
A.H. 1202 began on 13 Oct. A.D. 1787 (Sat.)=285
1 Shawwal   =267
                                            ———
                                            552
                                          —365
                                            ———
                                            187=5 July 1788,
                                                  Thursday.

vi. *To find Christian dates between 15 October 1582 and 14 September 1752 according to the Julian, or Old, Style.*

As has been said, England did not adopt the Gregorian, or New Style, until 14 September 1752. By this time the error in her calendar was eleven days, and this was corrected by making 14 September follow immediately upon 2 September in that year. In the present tables calculation has been based upon the Gregorian Calendar from its inception. If between 15 October 1582 and 14 September 1752 it is wished to calculate in the Julian, or Old, Style ten days should be added to the day of the Christian Year as shown in *Table Three* between 1 January 1583 and 31 December 1699 inclusive and eleven days between 29 February 1700 and 2 September 1752 inclusive. During this period there was a consequent difference in the days of the week. Thus from 1583 until 1752 the last column of *Table One* shows in brackets the day of the week on which 1 January fell according to the Old Style. To ascertain the day of the week during 1582 the Old Style follows the calendar for a common year in which 1 January fell on a Saturday. As to the New Style, a separate calendar, showing also the day of the year, is given in *Table Five*.

vii. *To find a Muslim date from a Christian date.*

This is done by simply reversing the processes already described. The Christian date should first be written down in full, followed by the day of the year, as ascertained from *Table Three*. *Table One* should then be consulted to find out the corresponding Muslim Year. This should be written down together with the number of days shown to have elapsed in the Christian Year on the day on which it began. If the number of days elapsed in the Christian Year on 1 Muharram is less than the number of days of the year on the date concerned, then it should be deducted from the latter.

For example:

1 September A.D. 1930   = 244
A.H. 1349 began 29 May A.D. 1930 = 148

$$96 = 7 \text{ Rabi' al-Akhir A.H. 1349.}$$

The same method is employed in Leap Years, care having been taken to consult the third column of *Table Three* to ascertain the day of the Christian Year.

It occurs, however, that inspection of *Table Three* will show that the relevant Muslim Year began in the preceding Christian Year to that under reference. Thus, for example, the Muslim Year in which 4 September 1946 occurred began in 1945. In this case the number of days reached in the Christian Year is first ascertained and written down. The preceding Muslim Year is then written down with the Christian date on which 1 Muharram fell, followed by the number of days then elapsed in the Christian Year. The latter number is then deducted from the total number of days in the relevant Christian Year, 365 in common years, and 366 in Leap Years. The result is then added to the number of days reached in the Christian Year, this result giving the number of days which has been reached in the Muslim Year. *Table Two* is then searched for the day of the month corresponding to this result.

For example:

4 September 1946   247
A.H. 1366 began 6 December A.D. 1945 + 339 from 365 =   26

                                        273
                       = 7 Shawwal A.H. 1366.

viii. *Use of Tables Six to Eight.*

Table Six gives the dates of the principal Muslim Festivals, all of which begin on fixed dates. The Christian dates on which they occur can rapidly be found for each year by reference to the preceding tables. It should be remembered that all of these festivals begin at sundown.
Tables Seven and Eight list the principal Christian Fixed and Movable Festivals. In finding the corresponding Muslim dates it is to be recollected that all these festivals begin at midnight and not at sunset.

TABLE ONE: **The Hijra Year and the Christian Year**

Hijra Year	Christian date of Muharram 1	Number of days elapsed in the Christian Year	Day on which the Christian Year began
1	16 July 622	196	F
2	5 July 623	185	S
3	*24 June 624	175	S
4	13 June 625	163	Tu
5	2 June 626	152	W
6	23 May 627	141	Th
7	*11 May 628	131	F
8	1 May 629	120	S
9	20 April 630	109	M
10	9 April 631	98	Tu
11	*29 March 632	88	W
12	18 March 633	76	F
13	7 March 634	65	S
14	25 February 635	55	S
15	*14 February 636	44	M
16	2 February 637	32	W
17	23 January 638	22	Th
18	12 January 639	11	F
19	* 2 January 640	1	S
20	*21 December 640	355	S
21	10 December 641	343	M
22	30 November 642	333	Tu
23	19 November 643	322	W
24	* 7 November 644	311	Th
25	28 October 645	300	S
26	17 October 646	289	S
27	7 October 647	279	M
28	*25 September 648	268	Tu
29	14 September 649	256	Th
30	4 September 650	246	F
31	24 August 651	235	S

*A Leap Year.

14

Hijra Year	Christian date of Muharram 1	Number of days elapsed in the Christian Year	Day on which the Christian Year began
32	*12 August 652	224	S
33	2 August 653	213	Tu
34	22 July 654	202	W
35	11 July 655	191	Th
36	*30 June 656	181	F
37	19 June 657	169	S
38	9 June 658	159	M
39	29 May 659	148	Tu
40	*17 May 660	137	W
41	7 May 661	126	F
42	26 April 662	115	S
43	15 April 663	104	S
44	* 4 April 664	94	M
45	24 March 665	82	W
46	13 March 666	71	Th
47	3 March 667	61	F
48	*20 February 668	50	S
49	9 February 669	39	M
50	29 January 670	28	Tu
51	18 January 671	17	W
52	* 8 January 672	7	Th
53	*27 December 672	361	Th
54	16 December 673	349	S
55	6 December 674	339	S
56	25 November 675	328	M
57	*14 November 676	318	Tu
58	3 November 677	306	Th
59	23 October 678	295	F
60	13 October 679	285	S
61	* 1 October 680	274	S
62	20 September 681	262	Tu

*A Leap Year.

Hijra Year	Christian date of Muharram 1	Number of days elapsed in the Christian Year	Day on which the Christian Year began
63	10 September 682	252	W
64	30 August 683	241	Th
65	*18 August 684	230	F
66	8 August 685	219	S
67	28 July 686	208	M
68	18 July 687	198	Tu
69	* 6 July 688	187	W
70	25 June 689	175	F
71	15 June 690	165	S
72	4 June 691	154	S
73	*23 May 692	143	M
74	13 May 693	132	W
75	2 May 694	121	Th
76	21 April 695	110	F
77	*10 April 696	100	S
78	30 March 697	88	M
79	20 March 698	78	Tu
80	9 March 699	67	W
81	*26 February 700	56	Th
82	15 February 701	45	S
83	4 February 702	34	S
84	24 January 703	23	M
85	*14 January 704	13	Tu
86	2 January 705	1	Th
87	23 December 705	356	Th
88	12 December 706	345	F
89	1 December 707	334	S
90	*20 November 708	324	S
91	9 November 709	312	Tu
92	29 October 710	301	W
93	19 October 711	291	Th

*A Leap Year.

Hijra Year	Christian date of Muharram 1	Number of days elapsed in the Christian Year	Day on which the Christian Year began
94	* 7 October 712	280	F
95	26 September 713	268	S
96	16 September 714	258	M
97	5 September 715	247	Tu
98	*25 August 716	237	W
99	14 August 717	225	F
100	3 August 718	214	S
101	24 July 719	204	S
102	*12 July 720	193	M
103	1 July 721	181	W
104	21 June 722	171	Th
105	10 June 723	160	F
106	*29 May 724	149	S
107	19 May 725	138	M
108	8 May 726	127	Tu
109	28 April 727	117	W
110	*16 April 728	106	Th
111	5 April 729	94	S
112	26 March 730	84	S
113	15 March 731	73	M
114	* 3 March 732	62	Tu
115	21 February 733	51	Th
116	10 February 734	40	F
117	31 January 735	30	S
118	*20 January 736	19	S
119	8 January 737	7	Tu
120	29 December 737	362	Tu
121	18 December 738	351	W
122	7 December 739	340	Th
123	*26 November 740	330	F
124	15 November 741	318	S

*A Leap Year.

Hijra Year	Christian date of Muharram 1	Number of days elapsed in the Christian Year	Day on which the Christian Year began
125	4 November 742	307	M
126	25 October 743	297	Tu
127	*13 October 744	286	W
128	3 October 745	275	F
129	22 September 746	264	S
130	11 September 747	253	S
131	*31 August 748	243	M
132	20 August 749	231	W
133	9 August 750	220	Th
134	30 July 751	210	F
135	*18 July 752	198	S
136	7 July 753	187	M
137	27 June 754	177	Tu
138	16 June 755	166	W
139	* 5 June 756	156	Th
140	25 May 757	144	S
141	14 May 758	133	S
142	4 May 759	123	M
143	*22 April 760	111	Tu
144	11 April 761	100	Th
145	1 April 762	90	F
146	21 March 763	79	S
147	*10 March 764	68	S
148	27 February 765	57	Tu
149	16 February 766	46	W
150	6 February 767	36	Th
151	*26 January 768	25	F
152	14 January 769	13	S
153	4 January 770	3	M
154	24 December 770	357	M
155	13 December 771	346	Tu

*A Leap Year.

Hijra Year	Christian date of Muharram 1	Number of days elapsed in the Christian Year	Day on which the Christian Year began
156	* 2 December 772	336	W
157	21 November 773	324	F
158	11 November 774	314	S
159	31 October 775	303	☙
160	*19 October 776	292	M
161	9 October 777	281	W
162	28 September 778	270	Th
163	17 September 779	259	F
164	* 6 September 780	248	S
165	26 August 781	237	M
166	15 August 782	227	Tu
167	5 August 783	216	W
168	*24 July 784	205	Th
169	14 July 785	194	S
170	3 July 786	183	☙
171	22 June 787	172	M
172	*11 June 788	162	Tu
173	31 May 789	150	Th
174	20 May 790	139	F
175	10 May 791	129	S
176	*28 April 792	118	☙
177	18 April 793	107	Tu
178	7 April 794	96	W
179	27 March 795	85	Th
180	*16 March 796	75	F
181	5 March 797	63	☙
182	22 February 798	52	M
183	12 February 799	42	Tu
184	* 1 February 800	31	W
185	20 January 801	19	F
186	10 January 802	9	S

*A Leap Year.

TABLE ONE: THE HIJRA YEAR AND THE CHRISTIAN YEAR

Hijra Year	Christian date of Muharram 1	Number of days elapsed in the Christian Year	Day on which the Christian Year began
187	30 December 802	363	S
188	20 December 803	353	S
189	* 8 December 804	342	M
190	27 November 805	330	W
191	17 November 806	320	Th
192	6 November 807	309	F
193	*25 October 808	298	S
194	15 October 809	287	M
195	4 October 810	276	Tu
196	23 September 811	265	W
197	*12 September 812	255	Th
198	1 September 813	243	S
199	22 August 814	233	S
200	11 August 815	222	M
201	*30 July 816	211	Tu
202	20 July 817	200	Th
203	9 July 818	189	F
204	28 June 819	178	S
205	*17 June 820	168	S
206	6 June 821	156	Tu
207	27 May 822	146	W
208	16 May 823	135	Th
209	* 4 May 824	123	F
210	24 April 825	113	S
211	13 April 826	102	M
212	2 April 827	91	Tu
213	*22 March 828	81	W
214	11 March 829	69	F
215	25 February 830	58	S
216	18 February 831	48	S
217	* 7 February 832	37	M

*A Leap Year.

Hijra Year	Christian date of Muharram 1	Number of days elapsed in the Christian Year	Day on which the Christian Year began
218	27 January 833	26	W
219	16 January 834	15	Th
220	5 January 835	4	F
221	26 December 835	359	F
222	*14 December 836	347	S
223	3 December 837	336	M
224	23 November 838	326	Tu
225	12 November 839	315	W
226	*31 October 840	304	Th
227	21 October 841	293	S
228	10 October 842	282	⛎
229	30 September 843	272	M
230	*18 September 844	261	Tu
231	7 September 845	249	Th
232	28 August 846	239	F
233	17 August 847	228	S
234	* 5 August 848	216	⛎
235	26 July 849	206	Tu
236	15 July 850	195	W
237	5 July 851	185	Th
238	*23 June 852	174	F
239	12 June 853	162	⛎
240	2 June 854	152	M
241	22 May 855	141	Tu
242	*10 May 856	130	W
243	30 April 857	119	F
244	19 April 858	108	S
245	8 April 859	97	⛎
246	*28 March 860	87	M
247	17 March 861	75	W
248	7 March 862	65	Th

*A Leap Year.

Hijra Year	Christian date of Muharram 1	Number of days elapsed in the Christian Year	Day on which the Christian Year began
249	24 February 863	54	F
250	*13 February 864	44	S
251	2 February 865	32	M
252	22 January 866	21	Tu
253	11 January 867	10	W
254	* 1 January 868	0	Th
255	*20 December 868	354	Th
256	9 December 869	342	S
257	29 November 870	332	S
258	18 November 871	321	M
259	* 7 November 872	311	Tu
260	27 October 873	299	Th
261	16 October 874	288	F
262	6 October 875	278	S
263	*24 September 876	267	S
264	13 September 877	255	Tu
265	3 September 878	245	W
266	23 August 879	234	Th
267	*12 August 880	224	F
268	1 August 881	212	S
269	21 July 882	201	M
270	11 July 883	191	Tu
271	*29 June 884	180	W
272	18 June 885	168	F
273	8 June 886	158	S
274	28 May 887	147	S
275	*16 May 888	136	M
276	6 May 889	125	W
277	25 April 890	114	Th
278	15 April 891	104	F
279	* 3 April 892	93	S

*A Leap Year.

Hijra Year	Christian date of Muharram 1	Number of days elapsed in the Christian Year	Day on which the Christian Year began
280	23 March 893	81	M
281	13 March 894	71	Tu
282	2 March 895	60	W
283	*19 February 896	49	Th
284	8 February 897	38	S
285	28 January 898	27	S
286	17 January 899	16	M
287	* 7 January 900	6	Tu
288	*26 December 900	360	Tu
289	16 December 901	349	Th
290	5 December 902	338	F
291	24 November 903	327	S
292	*13 November 904	317	S
293	2 November 905	305	Tu
294	22 October 906	294	W
295	12 October 907	284	Th
296	*30 September 908	273	F
297	20 September 909	262	S
298	9 September 910	251	M
299	29 August 911	240	Tu
300	*18 August 912	230	W
301	7 August 913	218	F
302	27 July 914	207	S
303	17 July 915	197	S
304	* 5 July 916	186	M
305	24 June 917	174	W
306	14 June 918	164	Th
307	3 June 919	158	F
308	*23 May 920	143	S
309	12 May 921	131	M
310	1 May 922	120	Tu

*A Leap Year.

Hijra Year	Christian date of Muharram 1	Number of days elapsed in the Christian Year	Day on which the Christian Year began
311	21 April 923	110	W
312	* 9 April 924	99	Th
313	29 March 925	87	S
314	19 March 926	77	Ṣ
315	8 March 927	66	M
316	*25 February 928	55	Tu
317	14 February 929	44	Th
318	3 February 930	33	F
319	24 January 931	23	S
320	*13 January 932	12	Ṣ
321	1 January 933	0	Tu
322	22 December 933	355	Tu
323	11 December 934	344	W
324	30 November 935	333	Th
325	*19 November 936	323	F
326	8 November 937	311	Ṣ
327	29 October 938	301	M
328	18 October 939	291	Tu
329	* 6 October 940	279	W
330	26 September 941	268	F
331	15 September 942	257	S
332	4 September 943	246	Ṣ
333	*24 August 944	236	M
334	13 August 945	224	W
335	2 August 946	213	Th
336	23 July 947	203	F
337	*11 July 948	192	S
338	1 July 949	181	M
339	20 June 950	170	Tu
340	9 June 951	159	W
341	*29 May 952	149	Th

*A Leap Year.

Hijra Year	Christian date of Muharram 1	Number of days elapsed in the Christian Year	Day on which the Christian Year began
342	18 May 953	137	S
343	7 May 954	126	℈
344	27 April 955	116	M
345	*15 April 956	105	Tu
346	4 April 957	93	Th
347	25 March 958	83	F
348	14 March 959	72	S
349	* 3 March 960	62	℈
350	20 February 961	50	Tu
351	9 February 962	39	W
352	30 January 963	29	Th
353	*19 January 964	18	F
354	7 January 965	6	℈
355	28 December 965	361	℈
356	17 December 966	350	M
357	7 December 967	340	Tu
358	*25 November 968	329	W
359	14 November 969	317	F
360	4 November 970	307	S
361	24 October 971	296	℈
362	*12 October 972	285	M
363	2 October 973	274	W
364	21 September 974	263	Th
365	10 September 975	252	F
366	*30 August 976	242	S
367	19 August 977	231	M
368	9 August 978	221	Tu
369	29 July 979	209	W
370	*17 July 980	198	Th
371	7 July 981	187	S
372	26 June 982	176	℈

*A Leap Year.

C

Hijra Year	Christian date of Muharram 1	Number of days elapsed in the Christian Year	Day on which the Christian Year began
373	15 June 983	165	M
374	* 4 June 984	155	Tu
375	24 May 985	143	Th
376	13 May 986	133	F
377	3 May 987	123	S
378	*21 April 988	111	S
379	11 April 989	100	Tu
380	31 March 990	89	W
381	20 March 991	78	Th
382	* 9 March 992	68	F
383	26 February 993	56	S
384	15 February 994	45	M
385	5 February 995	34	Tu
386	*25 January 996	24	W
387	14 January 997	13	F
388	3 January 998	2	S
389	23 December 998	356	S
390	13 December 999	346	S
391	* 1 December 1000	335	M
392	20 November 1001	323	W
393	10 November 1002	313	Th
394	30 October 1003	302	F
395	*18 October 1004	291	S
396	8 October 1005	281	M
397	27 September 1006	269	Tu
398	17 September 1007	259	W
399	* 5 September 1008	248	Th
400	25 August 1009	236	S
401	15 August 1010	226	S
402	4 August 1011	215	M
403	*23 July 1012	204	Tu

*A Leap Year.

Hijra Year	Christian date of Muharram 1	Number of days elapsed in the Christian Year	Day on which the Christian Year began
404	13 July 1013	193	Th
405	3 July 1014	183	F
406	21 June 1015	171	S
407	*10 June 1016	161	♆
408	30 May 1017	149	Tu
409	20 May 1018	139	W
410	9 May 1019	128	Th
411	*27 April 1020	117	F
412	17 April 1021	106	♆
413	6 April 1022	95	M
414	26 March 1023	84	Tu
415	*15 March 1024	74	W
416	4 March 1025	62	F
417	22 February 1026	52	S
418	11 February 1027	41	♆
419	*31 January 1028	30	M
420	20 January 1029	19	W
421	9 January 1030	8	Th
422	29 December 1030	362	Th
423	19 December 1031	352	F
424	* 7 December 1032	341	S
425	26 November 1033	329	M
426	16 November 1034	319	Tu
427	5 November 1035	308	W
428	*25 October 1036	298	Th
429	14 October 1037	286	S
430	3 October 1038	275	♆
431	23 September 1039	265	M
432	*11 September 1040	254	Tu
433	31 August 1041	242	Th
434	21 August 1042	232	F

*A Leap Year.

Hijra Year	Christian date of Muharram 1	Number of days elapsed in the Christian Year	Day on which the Christian Year began
435	10 August 1043	221	S
436	*29 July 1044	210	S
437	19 July 1045	199	Tu
438	8 July 1046	188	W
439	28 June 1047	178	Th
440	*16 June 1048	167	F
441	5 June 1049	155	S
442	26 May 1050	145	M
443	15 May 1051	134	Tu
444	* 3 May 1052	123	W
445	23 April 1053	112	F
446	12 April 1054	101	S
447	2 April 1055	91	S
448	*21 March 1056	80	M
449	10 March 1057	68	W
450	28 February 1058	58	Th
451	17 February 1059	47	F
452	* 6 February 1060	36	S
453	26 January 1061	25	M
454	15 January 1062	14	Tu
455	4 January 1063	3	W
456	25 December 1063	358	W
457	*13 December 1064	347	Th
458	3 December 1065	336	S
459	22 November 1066	325	S
460	11 November 1067	314	M
461	*31 October 1068	304	Tu
462	20 October 1069	292	Th
463	9 October 1070	281	F
464	29 September 1071	271	S
465	*17 September 1072	260	S

*A Leap Year.

28

Hijra Year	Christian date of Muharram 1	Number of days elapsed in the Christian Year	Day on which the Christian Year began
466	6 September 1073	248	Tu
467	27 August 1074	238	W
468	16 August 1075	227	Th
469	* 5 August 1076	217	F
470	25 July 1077	205	S
471	14 July 1078	194	M
472	4 July 1079	184	Tu
473	*22 June 1080	173	W
474	11 June 1081	161	F
475	1 June 1082	151	S
476	21 May 1083	140	S
477	*10 May 1084	130	M
478	29 April 1085	118	W
479	18 April 1086	107	Th
480	8 April 1087	97	F
481	*27 March 1088	86	S
482	16 March 1089	74	M
483	6 March 1090	64	Tu
484	23 February 1091	53	W
485	*12 February 1092	42	Th
486	1 February 1093	31	S
487	21 January 1094	20	S
488	11 January 1095	10	M
489	31 December 1095	364	M
490	*19 December 1096	353	Tu
491	9 December 1097	342	Th
492	28 November 1098	331	F
493	17 November 1099	320	S
494	* 6 November 1100	310	S
495	26 October 1101	298	Tu
496	15 October 1102	287	W

*A Leap Year.

Hijra Year	Christian date of Muharram 1	Number of days elapsed in the Christian Year	Day on which the Christian Year began
497	5 October 1103	277	Th
498	*23 September 1104	265	F
499	13 September 1105	255	S
500	2 September 1106	244	M
501	22 August 1107	233	Tu
502	*11 August 1108	223	W
503	31 July 1109	211	F
504	20 July 1110	200	S
505	10 July 1111	190	S
506	*28 June 1112	179	M
507	18 June 1113	168	W
508	7 June 1114	157	Th
509	27 May 1115	146	F
510	*16 May 1116	136	S
511	5 May 1117	124	M
512	24 April 1118	113	Tu
513	14 April 1119	103	W
514	* 2 April 1120	92	Th
515	22 March 1121	80	S
516	12 March 1122	70	S
517	1 March 1123	59	M
518	*19 February 1124	49	Tu
519	7 February 1125	37	Th
520	27 January 1126	26	F
521	17 January 1127	16	S
522	* 6 January 1128	5	S
523	*25 December 1128	359	S
524	15 December 1129	348	Tu
525	4 December 1130	337	W
526	23 November 1131	326	Th
527	*12 November 1132	316	F

*A Leap Year.

Hijra Year	Christian date of Muharram 1	Number of days elapsed in the Christian Year	Day on which the Christian Year began
528	1 November 1133	304	Su
529	22 October 1134	294	M
530	11 October 1135	283	Tu
531	*29 September 1136	272	W
532	19 September 1137	261	F
533	8 September 1138	250	S
534	28 August 1139	239	Su
535	*17 August 1140	229	M
536	6 August 1141	217	W
537	27 July 1142	207	Th
538	16 July 1143	196	F
539	* 4 July 1144	185	S
540	24 June 1145	174	M
541	13 June 1146	163	Tu
542	2 June 1147	152	W
543	*22 May 1148	142	Th
544	11 May 1149	130	S
545	30 April 1150	119	Su
546	20 April 1151	109	M
547	* 8 April 1152	98	Tu
548	27 March 1153	87	Th
549	18 March 1154	76	F
550	7 March 1155	65	S
551	*25 February 1156	55	Su
552	13 February 1157	43	Tu
553	2 February 1158	32	W
554	23 January 1159	22	Th
555	*12 January 1160	11	F
556	*31 December 1160	365	F
557	21 December 1161	354	Su
558	10 December 1162	343	M

*A Leap Year.

Hijra Year	Christian date of Muharram 1	Number of days elapsed in the Christian Year	Day on which the Christian Year began
559	30 November 1163	333	Tu
560	*18 November 1164	322	W
561	7 November 1165	310	F
562	28 October 1166	300	S
563	17 October 1167	289	S
564	* 5 October 1168	278	M
565	25 September 1169	267	W
566	14 September 1170	256	Th
567	4 September 1171	246	F
568	*23 August 1172	235	S
569	12 August 1173	223	M
570	2 August 1174	213	Tu
571	22 July 1175	202	W
572	*10 July 1176	191	Th
573	30 June 1177	180	S
574	19 June 1178	169	S
575	8 June 1179	158	M
576	*28 May 1180	147	Tu
577	17 May 1181	136	Th
578	7 May 1182	126	F
579	26 April 1183	115	S
580	*14 April 1184	104	S
581	4 April 1185	93	Tu
582	24 March 1186	82	W
583	13 March 1187	71	Th
584	* 2 March 1188	61	F
585	19 February 1189	49	S
586	8 February 1190	38	M
587	29 January 1191	28	Tu
588	*18 January 1192	17	W
589	7 January 1193	6	F

*A Leap Year.

Hijra Year	Christian date of Muharram 1	Number of days elapsed in the Christian Year	Day on which the Christian Year began
590	27 December 1193	360	F
591	16 December 1194	349	S
592	6 December 1195	339	Ṡ
593	*24 November 1196	328	M
594	13 November 1197	316	W
595	3 November 1198	306	Th
596	23 October 1199	295	F
597	*12 October 1200	285	S
598	1 October 1201	274	M
599	20 September 1202	262	Tu
600	10 September 1203	252	W
601	*29 August 1204	241	Th
602	18 August 1205	229	S
603	8 August 1206	219	Ṡ
604	28 July 1207	208	M
605	*16 July 1208	197	Tu
606	6 July 1209	186	Th
607	25 June 1210	175	F
608	15 June 1211	166	S
609	* 3 June 1212	154	Ṡ
610	23 May 1213	142	Tu
611	13 May 1214	132	W
612	2 May 1215	121	Th
613	*20 April 1216	110	F
614	10 April 1217	99	Ṡ
615	30 March 1218	88	M
616	19 March 1219	77	Tu
617	* 8 March 1220	67	W
618	25 February 1221	55	F
619	15 February 1222	45	S
620	4 February 1223	34	Ṡ

*A Leap Year.

TABLE ONE: THE HIJRA YEAR AND THE CHRISTIAN YEAR

Hijra Year	Christian date of Muharram 1	Number of days elapsed in the Christian Year	Day on which the Christian Year began
621	*24 January 1224	23	M
622	13 January 1225	12	W
623	2 January 1226	1	Th
624	22 December 1226	355	Th
625	12 December 1227	345	F
626	*30 November 1228	334	S
627	20 November 1229	323	M
628	9 November 1230	312	Tu
629	29 October 1231	301	W
630	*18 October 1232	291	Th
631	7 October 1233	279	S
632	26 September 1234	268	Su
633	16 September 1235	258	M
634	* 4 September 1236	247	Tu
635	24 August 1237	235	Th
636	14 August 1238	225	F
637	3 August 1239	214	S
638	*23 July 1240	203	Su
639	12 July 1241	192	Tu
640	1 July 1242	181	W
641	21 June 1243	171	Th
642	* 9 June 1244	160	F
643	29 May 1245	148	Su
644	19 May 1246	138	M
645	8 May 1247	127	Tu
646	*26 April 1248	116	W
647	16 April 1249	105	F
648	5 April 1250	94	S
649	26 March 1251	85	Su
650	*14 March 1252	73	M
651	3 March 1253	61	W

*A Leap Year.

Hijra Year	Christian date of Muharram 1	Number of days elapsed in the Christian Year	Day on which the Christian Year began
652	21 February 1254	51	Th
653	10 February 1255	40	F
654	*30 January 1256	29	S
655	19 January 1257	18	M
656	8 January 1258	7	Tu
657	29 December 1258	362	Tu
658	18 December 1259	351	W
659	* 6 December 1260	340	Th
660	26 November 1261	329	S
661	15 November 1262	318	Ṣ
662	4 November 1263	307	M
663	*24 October 1264	297	Tu
664	13 October 1265	285	Th
665	2 October 1266	274	F
666	22 September 1267	264	S
667	*10 September 1268	253	Ṣ
668	31 August 1269	242	Tu
669	20 August 1270	231	W
670	9 August 1271	220	Th
671	*29 July 1272	210	F
672	18 July 1273	198	Ṣ
673	7 July 1274	187	M
674	27 June 1275	177	Tu
675	*15 June 1276	166	W
676	4 June 1277	155	F
677	25 May 1278	144	S
678	14 May 1279	133	Ṣ
679	* 3 May 1280	123	M
680	22 April 1281	111	W
681	11 April 1282	100	Th
682	1 April 1283	90	F

*A Leap Year.

Hijra Year	Christian date of Muharram 1	Number of days elapsed in the Christian Year	Day on which the Christian Year began
683	*20 March 1284	79	S
684	9 March 1285	67	M
685	27 February 1286	57	Tu
686	16 February 1287	46	W
687	* 6 February 1288	36	Th
688	25 January 1289	24	S
689	14 January 1290	13	S
690	4 January 1291	3	M
691	24 December 1291	357	M
692	*12 December 1292	346	Tu
693	2 December 1293	335	Th
694	21 November 1294	324	F
695	10 November 1295	313	S
696	*30 October 1296	303	S
697	19 October 1297	291	Tu
698	9 October 1298	281	W
699	28 September 1299	270	Th
700	*16 September 1300	259	F
701	5 September 1301	248	S
702	26 August 1302	237	M
703	15 August 1303	226	Tu
704	* 4 August 1304	216	W
705	24 July 1305	204	F
706	13 July 1306	193	S
707	3 July 1307	183	S
708	*21 June 1308	172	M
709	11 June 1309	161	W
710	31 May 1310	150	Th
711	20 May 1311	139	F
712	* 9 May 1312	129	S
713	28 April 1313	117	M

*A Leap Year.

Hijra Year	Christian date of Muharram 1	Number of days elapsed in the Christian Year	Day on which the Christian Year began
714	17 April 1314	106	Tu
715	7 April 1315	96	W
716	*26 March 1316	85	Th
717	16 March 1317	74	S
718	5 March 1318	63	S
719	22 February 1319	52	M
720	*12 February 1320	42	Tu
721	31 January 1321	30	Th
722	20 January 1322	19	F
723	10 January 1323	9	S
724	30 December 1323	363	S
725	*18 December 1324	352	S
726	8 December 1325	341	Tu
727	27 November 1326	330	W
728	17 November 1327	320	Th
729	* 5 November 1328	309	F
730	25 October 1329	297	S
731	15 October 1330	287	M
732	4 October 1331	276	Tu
733	*22 September 1332	265	W
734	12 September 1333	254	F
735	1 September 1334	243	S
736	21 August 1335	232	S
737	*10 August 1336	222	M
738	30 July 1337	210	W
739	20 July 1338	200	Th
740	9 July 1339	189	F
741	*27 June 1340	178	S
742	17 June 1341	167	M
743	6 June 1342	156	Tu
744	26 May 1343	145	W

*A Leap Year.

Hijra Year	Christian date of Muharram 1	Number of days elapsed in the Christian Year	Day on which the Christian Year began
745	*15 May 1344	135	Th
746	4 May 1345	123	S
747	24 April 1346	113	S
748	13 April 1347	102	M
749	* 1 April 1348	91	Tu
750	22 March 1349	80	Th
751	11 March 1350	69	F
752	28 February 1351	58	S
753	*18 February 1352	48	S
754	6 February 1353	36	Tu
755	26 January 1354	25	W
756	16 January 1355	15	Th
757	* 5 January 1356	4	F
758	*25 December 1356	359	F
759	15 December 1357	347	S
760	3 December 1358	336	M
761	23 November 1359	326	Tu
762	*11 November 1360	315	W
763	31 October 1361	303	F
764	21 October 1362	293	S
765	10 October 1363	282	S
766	*28 September 1364	271	M
767	18 September 1365	260	W
768	7 September 1366	249	Th
769	28 August 1367	239	F
770	*16 August 1368	228	S
771	5 August 1369	216	M
772	26 July 1370	206	Tu
773	15 July 1371	195	W
774	* 3 July 1372	184	Th
775	23 June 1373	173	S

*A Leap Year.

Hijra Year	Christian date of Muharram 1	Number of days elapsed in the Christian Year	Day on which the Christian Year began
776	12 June 1374	162	S
777	2 June 1375	152	M
778	*21 May 1376	141	Tu
779	10 May 1377	129	Th
780	30 April 1378	119	F
781	19 April 1379	108	S
782	* 7 April 1380	97	S
783	28 March 1381	86	Tu
784	17 March 1382	75	W
785	6 March 1383	64	Th
786	*24 February 1384	54	F
787	12 February 1385	42	S
788	2 February 1386	32	M
789	22 January 1387	21	Tu
790	*11 January 1388	10	W
791	*31 December 1388	365	W
792	20 December 1389	353	F
793	9 December 1390	342	S
794	29 November 1391	332	S
795	*17 November 1392	321	M
796	6 November 1393	309	W
797	27 October 1394	299	Th
798	16 October 1395	288	F
799	* 5 October 1396	278	S
800	24 September 1397	266	M
801	13 September 1398	255	Tu
802	3 September 1399	245	W
803	*22 August 1400	234	Th
804	11 August 1401	222	S
805	1 August 1402	212	S
806	21 July 1403	201	M

*A Leap Year.

Hijra Year	Christian date of Muharram 1	Number of days elapsed in the Christian Year	Day on which the Christian Year began
807	*10 July 1404	191	Tu
808	29 June 1405	179	Th
809	18 June 1406	168	F
810	8 June 1407	158	S
811	*27 May 1408	147	S
812	16 May 1409	136	Tu
813	6 May 1410	126	W
814	25 April 1411	114	Th
815	*13 April 1412	103	F
816	3 April 1413	92	S
817	23 March 1414	81	M
818	13 March 1415	71	Tu
819	* 1 March 1416	60	W
820	18 February 1417	48	F
821	8 February 1418	38	S
822	28 January 1419	27	S
823	*17 January 1420	16	M
824	6 January 1421	5	W
825	26 December 1421	359	W
826	15 December 1422	348	Th
827	5 December 1423	338	F
828	*23 November 1424	327	S
829	13 November 1425	316	M
830	2 November 1426	305	Tu
831	22 October 1427	294	W
832	*11 October 1428	284	Th
833	30 September 1429	272	S
834	19 September 1430	261	S
835	9 September 1431	251	M
836	*28 August 1432	240	Tu
837	18 August 1433	229	Th

*A Leap Year.

Hijra Year	Christian date of Muharram 1	Number of days elapsed in the Christian Year	Day on which the Christian Year began
838	7 August 1434	218	F
839	27 July 1435	207	S
840	*16 July 1436	197	S
841	5 July 1437	185	Tu
842	24 June 1438	174	W
843	14 June 1439	164	Th
844	* 2 June 1440	153	F
845	22 May 1441	141	S
846	12 May 1442	131	M
847	1 May 1443	120	Tu
848	*20 April 1444	110	W
849	9 April 1445	98	F
850	29 March 1446	87	S
851	19 March 1447	77	S
852	* 7 March 1448	66	M
853	24 February 1449	54	W
854	14 February 1450	44	Th
855	3 February 1451	33	F
856	*23 January 1452	22	S
857	12 January 1453	11	M
858	1 January 1454	0	Tu
859	22 December 1454	355	Tu
860	11 December 1455	344	W
861	*29 November 1456	333	Th
862	19 November 1457	322	S
863	8 November 1458	311	S
864	28 October 1459	300	M
865	*17 October 1460	290	Tu
866	6 October 1461	278	Th
867	26 September 1462	268	F
868	15 September 1463	257	S

*A Leap Year.

D

Hijra Year	Christian date of Muharram 1	Number of days elapsed in the Christian Year	Day on which the Christian Year began
869	* 3 September 1464	246	S
870	23 August 1465	234	Tu
871	13 August 1466	224	W
872	2 August 1467	213	Th
873	*22 July 1468	203	F
874	11 July 1469	191	S
875	30 June 1470	180	M
876	20 June 1471	170	Tu
877	* 8 June 1472	159	W
878	29 May 1473	148	F
879	18 May 1474	137	S
880	7 May 1475	126	S
881	*26 April 1476	116	M
882	15 April 1477	104	W
883	4 April 1478	93	Th
884	25 March 1479	83	F
885	*13 March 1480	72	S
886	2 March 1481	60	M
887	20 February 1482	50	Tu
888	9 February 1483	39	W
889	*30 January 1484	29	Th
890	18 January 1485	17	S
891	7 January 1486	6	S
892	28 December 1486	361	S
893	17 December 1487	350	M
894	* 5 December 1488	339	Tu
895	25 November 1489	328	Th
896	14 November 1490	317	F
897	4 November 1491	307	S
898	*23 October 1492	296	S
899	12 October 1493	284	Tu

*A Leap Year.

TABLE ONE: THE HIJRA YEAR AND THE CHRISTIAN YEAR

Hijra Year	Christian date of Muharram 1	Number of days elapsed in the Christian Year	Day on which the Christian Year began
900	2 October 1494	274	W
901	21 September 1495	263	Th
902	* 9 September 1496	252	F
903	30 August 1497	241	S
904	19 August 1498	230	M
905	8 August 1499	219	Tu
906	*28 July 1500	209	W
907	17 July 1501	197	F
908	7 July 1502	188	S
909	26 June 1503	176	S
910	*14 June 1504	165	M
911	4 June 1505	154	W
912	24 May 1506	143	Th
913	13 May 1507	132	F
914	* 2 May 1508	122	S
915	21 April 1509	110	M
916	10 April 1510	99	Tu
917	31 March 1511	89	W
918	*19 March 1512	78	Th
919	9 March 1513	67	S
920	26 February 1514	56	S
921	15 February 1515	46	M
922	* 5 February 1516	35	Tu
923	24 January 1517	23	Th
924	13 January 1518	12	F
925	3 January 1519	2	S
926	23 December 1519	356	S
927	*12 December 1520	346	S
928	1 December 1521	334	Tu
929	20 November 1522	323	W
930	10 November 1523	313	Th

*A Leap Year.

Hijra Year	Christian date of Muharram 1	Number of days elapsed in the Christian Year	Day on which the Christian Year began
931	*29 October 1524	302	F
932	18 October 1525	290	S
933	8 October 1526	280	M
934	27 October 1527	269	Tu
935	*15 September 1528	258	W
936	5 September 1529	247	F
937	25 August 1530	236	S
938	15 August 1531	226	S
939	* 3 August 1532	215	M
940	23 July 1533	203	W
941	13 July 1534	193	Th
942	2 July 1535	182	F
943	*20 June 1536	171	S
944	10 June 1537	161	M
945	30 May 1538	149	Tu
946	19 May 1539	138	W
947	* 8 May 1540	128	Th
948	27 April 1541	116	S
949	17 April 1542	106	S
950	6 April 1543	95	M
951	*25 March 1544	84	Tu
952	15 March 1545	73	Th
953	4 March 1546	62	F
954	21 February 1547	51	S
955	*11 February 1548	41	S
956	30 January 1549	29	Tu
957	20 January 1550	19	W
958	9 January 1551	8	Th
959	29 December 1551	362	Th
960	*18 December 1552	352	W
961	7 December 1553	340	F

*A Leap Year.

Hijra Year	Christian date of Muharram 1	Number of days elapsed in the Christian Year	Day on which the Christian Year began (O.S. in brackets)
962	26 November 1554	329	S
963	16 November 1555	319	S
964	* 4 November 1556	308	M
965	24 October 1557	296	W
966	14 October 1558	286	Th
967	3 October 1559	275	F
968	*22 September 1560	265	S
969	11 September 1561	253	M
970	31 August 1562	242	Tu
971	21 August 1563	232	W
972	* 9 August 1564	221	Th
973	29 July 1565	209	S
974	19 July 1566	199	S
975	8 July 1567	188	M
976	*26 June 1568	177	Tu
977	16 June 1569	166	Th
978	5 June 1570	155	F
979	26 May 1571	145	S
980	*14 May 1572	134	S
981	3 May 1573	122	Tu
982	23 April 1574	112	W
983	12 April 1575	101	Th
984	*31 March 1576	90	F
985	21 March 1577	79	S
986	10 March 1578	68	M
987	28 February 1579	58	Tu
988	*17 February 1580	47	W
989	5 February 1581	35	F
990	26 January 1582	25	S
991	25 January 1583	24	Th (S)
992	*14 January 1584	13	F (M)

*A Leap Year.

Hijra Year	Christian date of Muharram 1	Number of days elapsed in the Christian Year	Day on which the Christian Year began (O.S. in brackets)
993	3 January 1585	2	Su (W)
994	23 December 1585	356	Su (W)
995	12 December 1586	345	M (Th)
996	2 December 1587	335	Tu (F)
997	*20 November 1588	324	W (S)
998	10 November 1589	313	F (M)
999	30 October 1590	302	S (Tu)
1000	19 October 1591	291	Su (W)
1001	* 8 October 1592	281	M (Th)
1002	27 September 1593	269	W (S)
1003	16 September 1594	258	Th (Su)
1004	6 September 1595	248	F (M)
1005	*28 August 1596	237	S (Tu)
1006	14 August 1597	225	M (Th)
1007	4 August 1598	215	Tu (F)
1008	24 July 1599	204	W (S)
1009	*13 July 1600	194	Th (Su)
1010	2 July 1601	182	S (Tu)
1011	21 June 1602	171	Su (W)
1012	11 June 1603	161	M (Th)
1013	*30 May 1604	150	Tu (F)
1014	19 May 1605	138	Th (Su)
1015	9 May 1606	128	F (M)
1016	28 April 1607	117	S (Tu)
1017	*17 April 1608	107	Su (W)
1018	6 April 1609	95	Tu (F)
1019	26 March 1610	84	W (S)
1020	16 March 1611	74	Th (Su)
1021	* 4 March 1612	63	F (M)
1022	21 February 1613	51	Su (W)
1023	11 February 1614	41	M (Th)

*A Leap Year.

Hijra Year	Christian date of Muharram 1	Number of days elapsed in the Christian Year	Day on which the Christian Year began (O.S. in brackets)
1024	31 January 1615	30	Tu (F)
1025	*20 January 1616	19	W (S)
1026	9 January 1617	8	F (M)
1027	29 December 1617	362	F (M)
1028	19 December 1618	352	S (Tu)
1029	8 December 1619	341	𝕊 (W)
1030	*26 November 1620	330	M (Th)
1031	16 November 1621	319	W (S)
1032	5 November 1622	308	Th (𝕊)
1033	25 October 1623	297	F (M)
1034	*14 October 1624	287	S (Tu)
1035	3 October 1625	275	M (Th)
1036	22 September 1626	264	Tu (F)
1037	12 September 1627	254	W (S)
1038	*31 August 1628	243	Th (𝕊)
1039	21 August 1629	232	S (Tu)
1040	10 August 1630	221	𝕊 (W)
1041	30 July 1631	210	M (Th)
1042	*19 July 1632	200	Tu (F)
1043	8 July 1633	188	Th (𝕊)
1044	27 June 1634	177	F (M)
1045	17 June 1635	167	S (Tu)
1046	* 5 June 1636	156	𝕊 (W)
1047	26 May 1637	145	Tu (F)
1048	15 May 1638	134	W (S)
1049	4 May 1639	123	Th (𝕊)
1050	*23 April 1640	113	F (M)
1051	12 April 1641	101	𝕊 (W)
1052	1 April 1642	90	M (Th)
1053	22 March 1643	80	Tu (F)
1054	*10 March 1644	69	W (S)

*A Leap Year.

Hijra Year	Christian date of Muharram 1	Number of days elapsed in the Christian Year	Day on which the Christian Year began (O.S. in brackets)
1055	27 February 1645	57	F (M)
1056	17 February 1646	47	S (Tu)
1057	6 February 1647	36	S̄ (W)
1058	*27 January 1648	26	M (Th)
1059	15 January 1649	14	W (S)
1060	4 January 1650	3	Th (S̄)
1061	25 December 1650	358	Th (S̄)
1062	14 December 1651	347	F (M)
1063	* 2 December 1652	336	S (Tu)
1064	22 November 1653	325	M (Th)
1065	11 November 1654	314	Tu (F)
1066	31 October 1655	303	W (S)
1067	*20 October 1656	293	Th (S̄)
1068	9 October 1657	281	S (Tu)
1069	29 September 1658	271	S̄ (W)
1070	18 September 1659	260	M (Th)
1071	* 6 September 1660	249	Tu (F)
1072	27 August 1661	238	Th (S̄)
1073	16 August 1662	227	F (M)
1074	5 August 1663	216	S (Tu)
1075	*25 July 1664	206	S̄ (W)
1076	14 July 1665	194	Tu (F)
1077	4 July 1666	184	W (S)
1078	23 June 1667	173	Th (S̄)
1079	*11 June 1668	162	F (M)
1080	1 June 1669	151	S̄ (W)
1081	21 May 1670	140	M (Th)
1082	10 May 1671	129	Tu (F)
1083	*29 April 1672	119	W (S)
1084	18 April 1673	107	F (M)
1085	7 April 1674	96	S (Tu)

*A Leap Year.

TABLE ONE: THE HIJRA YEAR AND THE CHRISTIAN YEAR

Hijra Year	Christian date of Muharram 1	Number of days elapsed in the Christian Year	Day on which the Christian Year began (O.S. in brackets)
1086	28 March 1675	86	☉ (W)
1087	*16 March 1676	75	M (Th)
1088	6 March 1677	64	W (S)
1089	23 February 1678	53	Th (☉)
1090	12 February 1679	42	F (M)
1091	* 2 February 1680	32	S (Tu)
1092	21 January 1681	20	M (Th)
1093	10 January 1682	9	Tu (F)
1094	31 December 1682	364	Tu (F)
1095	20 December 1683	353	W (S)
1096	* 8 December 1684	342	Th (☉)
1097	28 November 1685	331	S (Tu)
1098	17 November 1686	320	☉ (W)
1099	7 November 1687	310	M (Th)
1100	*26 October 1688	299	Tu (F)
1101	15 October 1689	287	Th (☉)
1102	5 October 1690	277	F (M)
1103	24 September 1691	266	S (Tu)
1104	*12 September 1692	255	☉ (W)
1105	2 September 1693	244	Tu (F)
1106	22 August 1694	233	W (S)
1107	12 August 1695	223	Th (☉)
1108	*31 July 1696	212	F (M)
1109	20 July 1697	200	☉ (W)
1110	10 July 1698	190	M (Th)
1111	29 June 1699	179	Tu (F)
1112	†18 June 1700	168	W (S)
1113	8 June 1701	158	Th (M)
1114	28 May 1702	147	F (Tu)
1115	17 May 1703	136	S (W)

*A Leap Year.
†A Leap Year in the Old Style reckoning only.

Hijra Year	Christian date of Muharram 1	Number of days elapsed in the Christian Year	Day on which the Christian Year began (O.S. in brackets)
1116	* 6 May 1704	125	♋ (Th)
1117	25 April 1705	114	Tu (S)
1118	15 April 1706	104	W (S)
1119	4 April 1707	93	Th (M)
1120	*23 March 1708	82	F (Tu)
1121	13 March 1709	71	♋ (Th)
1122	2 March 1710	60	M (F)
1123	19 February 1711	49	Tu (S)
1124	* 9 February 1712	39	W (♋)
1125	28 January 1713	27	F (Tu)
1126	17 January 1714	16	S (W)
1127	7 January 1715	6	♋ (Th)
1128	27 December 1715	360	♋ (Th)
1129	*16 December 1716	350	M (F)
1130	5 December 1717	338	W (♋)
1131	24 November 1718	327	Th (M)
1132	14 November 1719	317	F (Tu)
1133	* 2 November 1720	306	S (W)
1134	22 October 1721	294	M (F)
1135	12 October 1722	284	Tu (S)
1136	1 October 1723	273	W (♋)
1137	*20 September 1724	263	Th (M)
1138	9 September 1725	251	S (W)
1139	29 August 1726	240	♋ (Th)
1140	19 August 1727	230	M (F)
1141	* 7 August 1728	219	Tu (S)
1142	27 July 1729	207	Th (M)
1143	17 July 1730	197	F (Tu)
1144	6 July 1731	186	S (W)
1145	*24 June 1732	175	♋ (Th)
1146	14 June 1733	164	Tu (S)

*A Leap Year.

TABLE ONE: THE HIJRA YEAR AND THE CHRISTIAN YEAR

Hijra Year	Christian date of Muharram 1	Number of days elapsed in the Christian Year	Day on which the Christian Year began (O.S. in brackets)
1147	3 June 1734	153	W (Su)
1148	24 May 1735	143	Th (M)
1149	*12 May 1736	132	F (Tu)
1150	1 May 1737	120	Su (Th)
1151	21 April 1738	110	M (F)
1152	10 April 1739	99	Tu (S)
1153	*29 March 1740	88	W (Su)
1154	19 March 1741	77	F (Tu)
1155	8 March 1742	66	S (W)
1156	25 February 1743	55	Su (Th)
1157	*15 February 1744	45	M (F)
1158	3 February 1745	33	W (Su)
1159	24 January 1746	23	Th (M)
1160	13 January 1747	12	F (Tu)
1161	* 2 January 1748	1	S (W)
1162	*22 December 1748	356	S (W)
1163	11 December 1749	344	M (F)
1164	30 November 1750	333	Tu (S)
1165	20 November 1751	323	W (Su)
1166	* 8 November 1752	312	Th (M)
1167	29 October 1753	301	S
1168	18 October 1754	290	Su
1169	7 October 1755	279	M
1170	*26 September 1756	269	Tu
1171	15 September 1757	257	Th
1172	4 September 1758	246	F
1173	25 August 1759	236	S
1174	*13 August 1760	215	Su
1175	2 August 1761	213	Tu
1176	23 July 1762	203	W
1177	12 July 1763	192	Th

A Leap Year.

Hijra Year	Christian date of Muharram 1	Number of days elapsed in the Christian Year	Day on which the Christian Year began
1178	* 1 July 1764	182	F
1179	20 June 1765	170	S
1180	9 June 1766	159	M
1181	30 May 1767	149	Tu
1182	*18 May 1768	138	W
1183	7 May 1769	126	F
1184	27 April 1770	116	S
1185	16 April 1771	105	S
1186	* 4 April 1772	94	M
1187	25 March 1773	83	W
1188	14 March 1774	72	Th
1189	4 March 1775	62	F
1190	*21 February 1776	51	S
1191	19 February 1777	39	M
1192	30 January 1778	29	Tu
1193	19 January 1779	18	W
1194	* 8 January 1780	7	Th
1195	*28 December 1780	362	Th
1196	17 December 1781	350	S
1197	7 December 1782	340	S
1198	26 November 1783	329	M
1199	*14 November 1784	318	Tu
1200	4 November 1785	307	Th
1201	24 October 1786	296	F
1202	13 October 1787	285	S
1203	* 2 October 1788	275	S
1204	21 September 1789	263	Tu
1205	10 September 1790	252	W
1206	31 August 1791	242	Th
1207	*19 August 1792	231	F
1208	9 August 1793	220	S

*A Leap Year.

TABLE ONE: THE HIJRA YEAR AND THE CHRISTIAN YEAR

Hijra Year	Christian date of Muharram 1	Number of days elapsed in the Christian Year	Day on which the Christian Year began
1209	29 July 1794	209	M
1210	18 July 1795	198	Tu
1211	* 7 July 1796	188	W
1212	26 June 1797	176	F
1213	15 June 1798	165	S
1214	5 June 1799	155	ﻉ
1215	25 May 1800	144	M
1216	14 May 1801	133	Tu
1217	4 May 1802	123	W
1218	23 April 1803	112	Th
1219	*12 April 1804	102	F
1220	1 April 1805	90	ﻉ
1221	21 March 1806	79	M
1222	11 March 1807	69	Tu
1223	*28 February 1808	58	W
1224	16 February 1809	46	F
1225	6 February 1810	36	S
1226	26 January 1811	25	ﻉ
1227	*16 January 1812	15	M
1228	4 January 1813	3	W
1229	24 December 1813	357	W
1230	14 December 1814	347	Th
1231	3 December 1815	336	F
1232	*21 November 1816	325	S
1233	11 November 1817	314	M
1234	31 October 1818	303	Tu
1235	20 October 1819	292	W
1236	* 9 October 1820	282	Th
1237	28 September 1821	270	S
1238	18 September 1822	260	ﻉ
1239	7 September 1823	249	M

*A Leap Year.

53

Hijra Year	Christian date of Muharram 1	Number of days elapsed in the Christian Year	Day on which the Christian Year began
1240	*26 August 1824	238	Tu
1241	16 August 1825	227	Th
1242	5 August 1826	216	F
1243	25 July 1827	205	S
1244	*14 July 1828	195	☙
1245	3 July 1829	183	Tu
1246	22 June 1830	172	W
1247	12 June 1831	162	Th
1248	*31 May 1832	151	F
1249	21 May 1833	140	☙
1250	10 May 1834	129	M
1251	29 April 1835	118	Tu
1252	*18 April 1836	108	W
1253	7 April 1837	96	F
1254	27 March 1838	85	S
1255	17 March 1839	75	☙
1256	* 5 March 1840	64	M
1257	23 February 1841	53	W
1258	12 February 1842	42	Th
1259	1 February 1843	31	F
1260	*22 January 1844	21	S
1261	10 January 1845	9	M
1262	30 December 1845	363	M
1263	20 December 1846	353	Tu
1264	9 December 1847	342	W
1265	*27 November 1848	331	Th
1266	17 November 1849	320	S
1267	6 November 1850	309	☙
1268	27 October 1851	299	M
1269	*15 October 1852	288	Tu
1270	4 October 1853	276	Th

*A Leap Year.

TABLE ONE: THE HIJRA YEAR AND THE CHRISTIAN YEAR

Hijra Year	Christian date of Muharram 1	Number of days elapsed in the Christian Year	Day on which the Christian Year began
1271	24 September 1854	266	F
1272	13 September 1855	255	S
1273	* 1 September 1856	244	S
1274	22 August 1857	233	Tu
1275	11 August 1858	222	W
1276	31 July 1859	211	Th
1277	*20 July 1860	201	F
1278	9 July 1861	189	S
1279	29 June 1862	179	M
1280	18 June 1863	168	Tu
1281	* 6 June 1864	157	W
1282	27 May 1865	146	F
1283	16 May 1866	135	S
1284	5 May 1867	124	S
1285	*24 April 1868	114	M
1286	13 April 1869	102	W
1287	3 April 1870	92	Th
1288	23 March 1871	81	F
1289	*11 March 1872	70	S
1290	1 March 1873	59	Tu
1291	18 February 1874	48	W
1292	7 February 1875	37	Th
1293	*28 January 1876	27	F
1294	16 January 1877	15	S
1295	5 January 1878	4	M
1296	26 December 1878	359	Tu
1297	15 December 1879	348	W
1298	* 4 December 1880	338	Th
1299	23 November 1881	326	S
1300	12 November 1882	315	S
1301	2 November 1883	305	M

*A Leap Year.

Hijra Year	Christian date of Muharram 1	Number of days elapsed in the Christian Year	Day on which the Christian Year began
1302	*21 October 1884	294	Tu
1303	10 October 1885	282	Th
1304	30 September 1886	272	F
1305	19 September 1887	261	S
1306	* 7 September 1888	250	⑉
1307	28 August 1889	239	Tu
1308	17 August 1890	228	W
1309	7 August 1891	218	Th
1310	*26 July 1892	207	F
1311	15 July 1893	195	⑉
1312	5 July 1894	185	M
1313	24 June 1895	174	Tu
1314	*12 June 1896	163	W
1315	2 June 1897	152	F
1316	22 May 1898	141	S
1317	12 May 1899	131	⑉
1318	1 May 1900	120	M
1319	20 May 1901	109	Tu
1320	10 April 1902	99	W
1321	30 March 1903	88	Th
1322	*18 March 1904	77	F
1323	8 March 1905	66	⑉
1324	25 February 1906	55	M
1325	14 February 1907	44	Tu
1326	* 4 February 1908	34	W
1327	23 January 1909	22	F
1328	13 January 1910	12	S
1329	2 January 1911	1	⑉
1330	22 December 1911	355	⑉
1331	*11 December 1912	345	M
1332	30 November 1913	333	W

*A Leap Year.

Hijra Year	Christian date of Muharram 1	Number of days elapsed in the Christian Year	Day on which the Christian Year began
1333	19 November 1914	322	Th
1334	9 November 1915	312	F
1335	*28 October 1916	301	S
1336	17 October 1917	289	M
1337	7 October 1918	279	Tu
1338	26 September 1919	268	W
1339	*15 September 1920	258	Th
1340	4 September 1921	246	S
1341	24 August 1922	235	⑤
1342	14 August 1923	225	M
1343	* 2 August 1924	214	Tu
1344	22 July 1925	202	Th
1345	12 July 1926	192	F
1346	1 July 1927	181	S
1347	*20 July 1928	171	⑤
1348	9 July 1929	159	Tu
1349	29 May 1930	148	W
1350	19 May 1931	138	Th
1351	* 7 May 1932	127	F
1352	26 April 1933	115	⑤
1353	16 April 1934	105	M
1354	5 April 1935	94	Tu
1355	*24 March 1936	83	W
1356	14 March 1937	72	F
1357	3 March 1938	61	S
1358	21 February 1939	51	⑤
1359	*10 February 1940	40	M
1360	29 January 1941	28	W
1361	19 January 1942	18	Th
1362	8 January 1943	7	F
1363	28 December 1943	361	F

*A Leap Year.

E

Hijra Year	Christian date of Muharram 1	Number of days elapsed in the Christian Year	Day on which the Christian Year began
1364	*17 December 1944	351	S
1365	6 December 1945	339	M
1366	25 November 1946	328	Tu
1367	15 November 1947	318	W
1368	* 3 November 1948	307	Th
1369	24 October 1949	296	S
1370	13 October 1950	285	S
1371	2 October 1951	274	M
1372	*21 September 1952	264	Tu
1373	10 September 1953	252	Th
1374	30 August 1954	241	F
1375	20 August 1955	231	S
1376	* 8 August 1956	220	S
1377	29 July 1957	209	Tu
1378	18 July 1958	198	W
1379	7 July 1959	187	Th
1380	*25 June 1960	176	F
1381	14 June 1961	164	S
1382	4 June 1962	154	M
1383	25 May 1963	144	Tu
1384	*13 May 1964	133	W
1385	2 May 1965	121	F
1386	22 April 1966	111	S
1387	11 April 1967	100	S
1388	*31 May 1968	90	M
1389	20 March 1969	78	W
1390	9 March 1970	67	Th
1391	27 February 1971	57	F
1392	*16 February 1972	46	S
1393	4 February 1973	34	M
1394	25 January 1974	24	Tu

*A Leap Year.

TABLE ONE: THE HIJRA YEAR AND THE CHRISTIAN YEAR

Hijra Year	Christian date of Muharram 1	Number of days elapsed in the Christian Year	Day on which the Christian Year began
1395	14 January 1975	13	W
1396	* 3 January 1976	2	Th
1397	*23 December 1976	357	Th
1398	12 December 1977	345	S
1399	2 December 1978	335	ẞ
1400	21 November 1979	324	M
1401	* 9 November 1980	313	Tu
1402	30 October 1981	302	Th
1403	19 October 1982	291	F
1404	8 October 1983	280	S
1405	*27 September 1984	270	ẞ
1406	16 September 1985	258	Tu
1407	6 September 1986	248	W
1408	26 August 1987	237	Th
1409	*14 August 1988	226	F
1410	4 August 1989	215	ẞ
1411	24 July 1990	204	M
1412	13 July 1991	193	Tu
1413	* 2 July 1992	183	W
1414	21 June 1993	171	F
1415	10 June 1994	160	S
1416	31 May 1995	150	ẞ
1417	*19 May 1996	139	M
1418	9 May 1997	128	W
1419	28 April 1998	117	Th
1420	17 April 1999	106	F
1421	* 6 April 2000	96	S

*A Leap Year.

TABLE TWO: **The Islamic Months and Days of the Year**

MUHARRAM		SAFAR		RABI' AL-AWAL	
Day of the Month	Year	Day of the Month	Year	Day of the Month	Year
1	1	1	31	1	60
2	2	2	32	2	61
3	3	3	33	3	62
4	4	4	34	4	63
5	5	5	35	5	64
6	6	6	36	6	65
7	7	7	37	7	66
8	8	8	38	8	67
9	9	9	39	9	68
10	10	10	40	10	69
11	11	11	41	11	70
12	12	12	42	12	71
13	13	13	43	13	72
14	14	14	44	14	73
15	15	15	45	15	74
16	16	16	46	16	75
17	17	17	47	17	76
18	18	18	48	18	77
19	19	19	49	19	78
20	20	20	50	20	79
21	21	21	51	21	80
22	22	22	52	22	81
23	23	23	53	23	82
24	24	24	54	24	83
25	25	25	55	25	84
26	26	26	56	26	85
27	27	27	57	27	86
28	28	28	58	28	87
29	29	29	59	29	88
30	30	—	—	30	89

RABI' AL-AKHIR		JUMADA AL-AULA		JUMADA AL-UKHRA	
Day of the		*Day of the*		*Day of the*	
Month	*Year*	*Month*	*Year*	*Month*	*Year*
1	90	1	119	1	149
2	91	2	120	2	150
3	92	3	121	3	151
4	93	4	122	4	152
5	94	5	123	5	153
6	95	6	124	6	154
7	96	7	125	7	155
8	97	8	126	8	156
9	98	9	127	9	157
10	99	10	128	10	158
11	100	11	129	11	159
12	101	12	130	12	160
13	102	13	131	13	161
14	103	14	132	14	162
15	104	15	133	15	163
16	105	16	134	16	164
17	106	17	135	17	165
18	107	18	136	18	166
19	108	19	137	19	167
20	109	20	138	20	168
21	110	21	139	21	169
22	111	22	140	22	170
23	112	23	141	23	171
24	113	24	142	24	172
25	114	25	143	25	173
26	115	26	144	26	174
27	116	27	145	27	175
28	117	28	146	28	176
29	118	29	147	29	177
—	—	30	148	—	—

RAJAB		SHA'BAN		RAMADHAN	
Day of the Month	Year	Day of the Month	Year	Day of the Month	Year
1	178	1	208	1	237
2	179	2	209	2	238
3	180	3	210	3	239
4	181	4	211	4	240
5	182	5	212	5	241
6	183	6	213	6	242
7	184	7	214	7	243
8	185	8	215	8	244
9	186	9	216	9	245
10	187	10	217	10	246
11	188	11	218	11	247
12	189	12	219	12	248
13	190	13	220	13	249
14	191	14	221	14	250
15	192	15	222	15	251
16	193	16	223	16	252
17	194	17	224	17	253
18	195	18	225	18	254
19	196	19	226	19	255
20	197	20	227	20	256
21	198	21	228	21	257
22	199	22	229	22	258
23	200	23	230	23	259
24	201	24	231	24	260
25	202	25	232	25	261
26	203	26	233	26	262
27	204	27	234	27	263
28	205	28	235	28	264
29	206	29	236	29	265
30	207	—	—	30	266

SHAWWAL		DHU AL-QA'DA		DHU AL-HIJJA	
Day of the		Day of the		Day of the	
Month	Year	Month	Year	Month	Year
I	267	I	296	I	326
2	268	2	297	2	327
3	269	3	298	3	328
4	270	4	299	4	329
5	271	5	300	5	330
6	272	6	301	6	331
7	273	7	302	7	332
8	274	8	303	8	333
9	275	9	304	9	334
10	276	10	305	10	335
11	277	11	306	11	336
12	278	12	307	12	337
13	279	13	308	13	338
14	280	14	309	14	339
15	281	15	310	15	340
16	282	16	311	16	341
17	283	17	312	17	342
18	284	18	313	18	343
19	285	19	314	19	344
20	286	20	315	20	345
21	287	21	316	21	346
22	288	22	317	22	347
23	289	23	318	23	348
24	290	24	319	24	349
25	291	25	320	25	350
26	292	26	321	26	351
27	293	27	322	27	352
28	294	28	323	28	353
29	295	29	324	29	354
—	—	30	325	—	—

The Christian Months and Days of the Year

	JANUARY			FEBRUARY			MARCH	
Day of the Year	Common Year	Leap Year	Day of the Year	Common Year	Leap Year	Day of the Year	Common Year	Leap Year
1	1	1	32	1	1	60	1	—
2	2	2	33	2	2	61	2	1
3	3	3	34	3	3	62	3	2
4	4	4	35	4	4	63	4	3
5	5	5	36	5	5	64	5	4
6	6	6	37	6	6	65	6	5
7	7	7	38	7	7	66	7	6
8	8	8	39	8	8	67	8	7
9	9	9	40	9	9	68	9	8
10	10	10	41	10	10	69	10	9
11	11	11	42	11	11	70	11	10
12	12	12	43	12	12	71	12	11
13	13	13	44	13	13	72	13	12
14	14	14	45	14	14	73	14	13
15	15	15	46	15	15	74	15	14
16	16	16	47	16	16	75	16	15
17	17	17	48	17	17	76	17	16
18	18	18	49	18	18	77	18	17
19	19	19	50	19	19	78	19	18
20	20	20	51	20	20	79	20	19
21	21	21	52	21	21	80	21	20
22	22	22	53	22	22	81	22	21
23	23	23	54	23	23	82	23	22
24	24	24	55	24	24	83	24	23
25	25	25	56	25	25	84	25	24
26	26	26	57	26	26	85	26	25
27	27	27	58	27	27	86	27	26
28	28	28	59	28	28	87	28	27
29	29	29	60	—	29	88	29	28
30	30	30				89	30	29
31	31	31				90	31	30
						91	—	31

	APRIL			MAY			JUNE	
Day of the Year	Common Year	Leap Year	Day of the Year	Common Year	Leap Year	Day of the Year	Common Year	Leap Year
91	1	—	121	1	—	152	1	—
92	2	1	122	2	1	153	2	1
93	3	2	123	3	2	154	3	2
94	4	3	124	4	3	155	4	3
95	5	4	125	5	4	156	5	4
96	6	5	126	6	5	157	6	5
97	7	6	127	7	6	158	7	6
98	8	7	128	8	7	159	8	7
99	9	8	129	9	8	160	9	8
100	10	9	130	10	9	161	10	9
101	11	10	131	11	10	162	11	10
102	12	11	132	12	11	163	12	11
103	13	12	133	13	12	164	13	12
104	14	13	134	14	13	165	14	13
105	15	14	135	15	14	166	15	14
106	16	15	136	16	15	167	16	15
107	17	16	137	17	16	168	17	16
108	18	17	138	18	17	169	18	17
109	19	18	139	19	18	170	19	18
110	20	19	140	20	19	171	20	19
111	21	20	141	21	20	172	21	20
112	22	21	142	22	21	173	22	21
113	23	22	143	23	22	174	23	22
114	24	23	144	24	23	175	24	23
115	25	24	145	25	24	176	25	24
116	26	25	146	26	25	177	26	25
117	27	26	147	27	26	178	27	26
118	28	27	148	28	27	179	28	27
119	29	28	149	29	28	180	29	28
120	30	29	150	30	29	181	30	29
121	—	30	151	31	30	182	—	30
			152	—	31			

65

	JULY			AUGUST			SEPTEMBER	
Day of the Year	Common Year	Leap Year	Day of the Year	Common Year	Leap Year	Day of the Year	Common Year	Leap Year
182	1	—	213	1	—	244	1	—
183	2	1	214	2	1	245	2	1
184	3	2	215	3	2	246	3	2
185	4	3	216	4	3	247	4	3
186	5	4	217	5	4	248	5	4
187	6	5	218	6	5	249	6	5
188	7	6	219	7	6	250	7	6
189	8	7	220	8	7	251	8	7
190	9	8	221	9	8	252	9	8
191	10	9	222	10	9	253	10	9
192	11	10	223	11	10	254	11	10
193	12	11	224	12	11	255	12	11
194	13	12	225	13	12	256	13	12
195	14	13	226	14	13	257	14	13
196	15	14	227	15	14	258	15	14
197	16	15	228	16	15	259	16	15
198	17	16	229	17	16	260	17	16
199	18	17	230	18	17	261	18	17
200	19	18	231	19	18	262	19	18
201	20	19	232	20	19	263	20	19
202	21	20	233	21	20	264	21	20
203	22	21	234	22	21	265	22	21
204	23	22	235	23	22	266	23	22
205	24	23	236	24	23	267	24	23
206	25	24	237	25	24	268	25	24
207	26	25	238	26	25	269	26	25
208	27	26	239	27	26	270	27	26
209	28	27	240	28	27	271	28	27
210	29	28	241	29	28	272	29	28
211	30	29	242	30	29	273	30	29
212	31	30	243	31	30	274	—	30
213	—	31	244	—	31			

	OCTOBER			NOVEMBER			DECEMBER	
Day of the Year	Common Year	Leap Year	Day of the Year	Common Year	Leap Year	Day of the Year	Common Year	Leap Year
274	1	—	305	1	—	335	1	—
275	2	1	306	2	1	336	2	1
276	3	2	307	3	2	337	3	2
277	4	3	308	4	3	338	4	3
278	5	4	309	5	4	339	5	4
279	6	5	310	6	5	340	6	5
280	7	6	311	7	6	341	7	6
281	8	7	312	8	7	342	8	7
282	9	8	313	9	8	343	9	8
283	10	9	314	10	9	344	10	9
284	11	10	315	11	10	345	11	10
285	12	11	316	12	11	346	12	11
286	13	12	317	13	12	347	13	12
287	14	13	318	14	13	348	14	13
288	15	14	319	15	14	349	15	14
289	16	15	320	16	15	350	16	15
290	17	16	321	17	16	351	17	16
291	18	17	322	18	17	352	18	17
292	19	18	323	19	18	353	19	18
293	20	19	324	20	19	354	20	19
294	21	20	325	21	20	355	21	20
295	22	21	326	22	21	356	22	21
296	23	22	327	23	22	357	23	22
297	24	23	328	24	23	358	24	23
298	25	24	329	25	24	359	25	24
299	26	25	330	26	25	360	26	25
300	27	26	331	27	26	361	27	26
301	28	27	332	28	27	362	28	27
302	29	28	333	29	28	363	29	28
303	30	29	334	30	29	364	30	29
304	31	30	335	—	30	365	31	30
305	—	31				366	—	31

Perpetual Calendar of the Days of the Week in the Christian Year

1. Common Years in which 1 January falls on a Sunday

	January	February	March
S	1 8 15 22 29	– 5 12 19 26	– 5 12 19 26
M	2 9 16 23 30	– 6 13 20 27	– 6 13 20 27
Tu	3 10 17 24 31	– 7 14 21 28	– 7 14 21 28
W	4 11 18 25 –	1 8 15 22 –	1 8 15 22 29
Th	5 12 19 26 –	2 9 16 23 –	2 9 16 23 30
F	6 13 20 27 –	3 10 17 24 –	3 10 17 24 31
S	7 14 21 28 –	4 11 18 25 –	4 11 18 25 –

	April	May	June
S	– 2 9 16 23 30	– 7 14 21 28	– 4 11 18 25
M	– 3 10 17 24 –	1 8 15 22 29	– 5 12 19 26
Tu	– 4 11 18 25 –	2 9 16 23 30	– 6 13 20 27
W	– 5 12 19 26 –	3 10 17 24 31	– 7 14 21 28
Th	– 6 13 20 27 –	4 11 18 25 –	1 8 15 22 29
F	– 7 14 21 28 –	5 12 19 26 –	2 9 16 23 30
S	1 8 15 22 29 –	6 13 20 27 –	3 10 17 24 –

	July	August	September
S	– 2 9 16 23 30	– 6 13 20 27	– 3 10 17 24
M	– 3 10 17 24 31	– 7 14 21 28	– 4 11 18 25
Tu	– 4 11 18 25 –	1 8 15 22 29	– 5 12 19 26
W	– 5 12 19 26 –	2 9 16 23 30	– 6 13 20 27
Th	– 6 13 20 27 –	3 10 17 24 31	– 7 14 21 28
F	– 7 14 21 28 –	4 11 18 25 –	1 8 15 22 29
S	1 8 15 22 29 –	5 12 19 26 –	2 9 16 23 30

	October	November	December
S	1 8 15 22 29	– 5 12 19 26	– 3 10 17 24 31
M	2 9 16 23 30	– 6 13 20 27	– 4 11 18 25 –
Tu	3 10 17 24 31	– 7 14 21 28	– 5 12 19 26 –
W	4 11 18 25 –	1 8 15 22 29	– 6 13 20 27 –
Th	5 12 19 26 –	2 9 16 23 30	– 7 14 21 28 –
F	6 13 20 27 –	3 10 17 24 –	1 8 15 22 29 –
S	7 14 21 28 –	4 11 18 25 –	2 9 16 23 30 –

2. *Leap Years in which 1 January falls on a Sunday*

	January	February	March
S	1 8 15 22 29	– 5 12 19 26	– 4 11 18 25
M	2 9 16 23 30	– 6 13 20 27	– 5 12 19 26
Tu	3 10 17 24 31	– 7 14 21 28	– 6 13 20 27
W	4 11 18 25 —	1 8 15 22 29	– 7 14 21 28
Th	5 12 19 26 —	2 9 16 23 —	1 8 15 22 29
F	6 13 20 27 —	3 10 17 24 —	2 9 16 23 30
S	7 14 21 28 —	4 11 18 25 —	3 10 17 24 31

	April	May	June
S	1 8 15 22 29	– 6 13 20 27	– 3 10 17 24
M	2 9 16 23 30	– 7 14 21 28	– 4 11 18 25
Tu	3 10 17 24 —	1 8 15 22 29	– 5 12 19 26
W	4 11 18 25 —	2 9 16 23 30	– 6 13 20 27
Th	5 12 19 26 —	3 10 17 24 31	– 7 14 21 28
F	6 13 20 27 —	4 11 18 25 —	1 8 15 22 29
S	7 14 21 28 —	5 12 19 26 —	2 9 16 23 30

	July	August	September
S	1 8 15 22 29	– 5 12 19 26	– 2 9 16 23 30
M	2 9 16 23 30	– 6 13 20 27	– 3 10 17 24 —
Tu	3 10 17 24 31	– 7 14 21 28	– 4 11 18 25 —
W	4 11 18 25 —	1 8 15 22 29	– 5 12 19 26 —
Th	5 12 19 26 —	2 9 16 23 30	– 6 13 20 27 —
F	6 13 20 27 —	3 10 17 24 31	– 7 14 21 28 —
S	7 14 21 28 —	4 11 18 25 —	1 8 15 22 29 —

	October	November	December
S	– 7 14 21 28	– 4 11 18 25	– 2 9 16 23 30
M	1 8 15 22 29	– 5 12 19 26	– 3 10 17 24 31
Tu	2 9 16 23 30	– 6 13 20 27	– 4 11 18 25 —
W	3 10 17 24 31	– 7 14 21 28	– 5 12 19 26 —
Th	4 11 18 25 —	1 8 15 22 29	– 6 13 20 27 —
F	5 12 19 26 —	2 9 16 23 30	– 7 14 21 28 —
S	6 13 20 27 —	3 10 17 24 —	1 8 15 22 29 —

3. Common Years in which 1 January falls on a Monday

	January	February	March
S	– 7 14 21 28	– 4 11 18 25	– 4 11 18 25
M	1 8 15 22 29	– 5 12 19 26	– 5 12 19 26
Tu	2 9 16 23 30	– 6 13 20 27	– 6 13 20 27
W	3 10 17 24 31	– 7 14 21 28	– 7 14 21 28
Th	4 11 18 25 –	1 8 15 22 –	1 8 15 22 29
F	5 12 19 26 –	2 9 16 23 –	2 9 16 23 30
S	6 13 20 27 –	3 10 17 24 –	3 10 17 24 31

	April	May	June
S	1 8 15 22 29	– 6 13 20 27	– 3 10 17 24
M	2 9 16 23 30	– 7 14 21 28	– 4 11 18 25
Tu	3 10 17 24 –	1 8 15 22 29	– 5 12 19 26
W	4 11 18 25 –	2 9 16 23 30	– 6 13 20 27
Th	5 12 19 26 –	3 10 17 24 31	– 7 14 21 28
F	6 13 20 27 –	4 11 18 25 –	1 8 15 22 29
S	7 14 21 28 –	5 12 19 26 –	2 9 16 23 30

	July	August	September
S	1 8 15 22 29	– 5 12 19 26	– 2 9 16 23 30
M	2 9 16 23 30	– 6 13 20 27	– 3 10 17 24
Tu	3 10 17 24 31	– 7 14 21 28	– 4 11 18 25 –
W	4 11 18 25 –	1 8 15 22 29	– 5 12 19 26 –
Th	5 12 19 26 –	2 9 16 23 30	– 6 13 20 27 –
F	6 13 20 27 –	3 10 17 24 31	– 7 14 21 28 –
S	7 14 21 28 –	4 11 18 25 –	1 8 15 22 29 –

	October	November	December
S	– 7 14 21 28	– 4 11 18 25	– 2 9 16 23 30
M	1 8 15 22 29	– 5 12 19 26	– 3 10 17 24 31
Tu	2 9 16 23 30	– 6 13 20 27	– 4 11 18 25 –
W	3 10 17 24 31	– 7 14 21 28	– 5 12 19 26 –
Th	4 11 18 25 –	1 8 15 22 29	– 6 13 20 27 –
F	5 12 19 26 –	2 9 16 23 30	– 7 14 21 28 –
S	6 13 20 27 –	3 10 17 24 –	1 8 15 22 29 –

4. Leap Years in which 1 January falls on a Monday

	January						February					March					
S	–	7	14	21	28		–	4	11	18	25	–	3	10	17	24	31
M	1	8	15	22	29		–	5	12	19	26	–	4	11	18	25	–
Tu	2	9	16	23	30		–	6	13	20	27	–	5	12	19	26	–
W	3	10	17	24	31		–	7	14	21	28	–	6	13	20	27	–
Th	4	11	18	25	–		1	8	15	22	29	–	7	14	21	28	–
F	5	12	19	26	–		2	9	16	23	–	1	8	15	22	29	–
S	6	13	20	27	–		3	10	17	24	–	2	9	16	23	30	–

	April						May					June					
S	–	7	14	21	28		–	5	12	19	26	–	2	9	16	23	30
M	1	8	15	22	29		–	6	13	20	27	–	3	10	17	24	–
Tu	2	9	16	23	30		–	7	14	21	28	–	4	11	18	25	–
W	3	10	17	24	–		1	8	15	22	29	–	5	12	19	26	–
Th	4	11	18	25	–		2	9	16	23	30	–	6	13	20	27	–
F	5	12	19	26	–		3	10	17	24	31	–	7	14	21	28	–
S	6	13	20	27	–		4	11	18	25	–	1	8	15	22	29	–

	July						August					September					
S	–	7	14	21	28		–	4	11	18	25	1	8	15	22	29	
M	1	8	15	22	29		–	5	12	19	26	2	9	16	23	30	
Tu	2	9	16	23	30		–	6	13	20	27	3	10	17	24	–	
W	3	10	17	24	31		–	7	14	21	28	4	11	18	25	–	
Th	4	11	18	25	–		1	8	15	22	29	5	12	19	26	–	
F	5	12	19	26	–		2	9	16	23	30	6	13	20	27	–	
S	6	13	20	27	–		3	10	17	24	31	7	14	21	28	–	

	October						November					December					
S	–	6	13	20	27		–	3	10	17	24	1	8	15	22	29	
M	–	7	14	21	28		–	4	11	18	25	2	9	16	23	30	
Tu	1	8	15	22	29		–	5	12	19	26	3	10	17	24	31	
W	2	9	16	23	30		–	6	13	20	27	4	11	18	25	–	
Th	3	10	17	24	31		–	7	14	21	28	5	12	19	26	–	
F	4	11	18	25	–		1	8	15	22	29	6	13	20	27	–	
S	5	12	19	26	–		2	9	16	23	30	7	14	21	28	–	

TABLE FOUR: PERPETUAL CALENDAR OF THE DAYS OF THE WEEK IN THE CHRISTIAN YEAR

5. Common Years in which 1 January falls on a Tuesday

	January	February	March
Su	– 6 13 20 27	– 3 10 17 24	– 3 10 17 24 31
M	– 7 14 21 28	– 4 11 18 25	– 4 11 18 25 —
Tu	1 8 15 22 29	– 5 12 19 26	– 5 12 19 26 —
W	2 9 16 23 30	– 6 13 20 27	– 6 13 20 27 —
Th	3 10 17 24 31	– 7 14 21 28	– 7 14 21 28 —
F	4 11 18 25 —	1 8 15 22 —	1 8 15 22 29 —
S	5 12 19 26 —	2 9 16 23 —	2 9 16 23 30 —

	April	May	June
Su	– 7 14 21 28	– 5 12 19 26	– 2 9 16 23 30
M	1 8 15 22 29	– 6 13 20 27	– 3 10 17 24
T	2 9 16 23 30	– 7 14 21 28	– 4 11 18 25 —
W	3 10 17 24 —	1 8 15 22 29	– 5 12 19 26 —
Th	4 11 18 25 —	2 9 16 23 30	– 6 13 20 27 —
F	5 12 19 26 —	3 10 17 24 31	– 7 14 21 28 —
S	6 13 20 27 —	4 11 18 25 —	1 8 15 22 29 —

	July	August	September
Su	– 7 14 21 28	– 4 11 18 25	1 8 15 22 29
M	1 8 15 22 29	– 5 12 19 26	2 9 16 23 30
Tu	2 9 16 23 30	– 6 13 20 27	3 10 17 24 —
W	3 10 17 24 31	– 7 14 21 28	4 11 18 25 —
Th	4 11 18 25 —	1 8 15 22 29	5 12 19 26 —
F	5 12 19 26 —	2 9 16 23 30	6 13 20 27 —
S	6 13 20 27 —	3 10 17 24 31	7 14 21 28 —

	October	November	December
Su	– 6 13 20 27	– 3 10 17 24	1 8 15 22 29
M	– 7 14 21 28	– 4 11 18 25	2 9 16 23 30
Tu	1 8 15 22 29	– 5 12 19 26	3 10 17 24 31
W	2 9 16 23 30	– 6 13 20 27	4 11 18 25 —
Th	3 10 17 24 31	– 7 14 21 28	5 12 19 26 —
F	4 11 18 25 —	1 8 15 22 29	6 13 20 27 —
S	5 12 19 26 —	2 9 16 23 30	7 14 21 28 —

6. Leap Years in which 1 January falls on a Tuesday

	January					February					March				
☉	-	6	13	20	27	-	3	10	17	24	-	2	9	16	23	30
M	-	7	14	21	28	-	4	11	18	25	-	3	10	17	24	31
Tu	1	8	15	22	29	-	5	12	19	26	-	4	11	18	25	—
W	2	9	16	23	30	-	6	13	20	27	-	5	12	19	26	—
Th	3	10	17	24	31	-	7	14	21	28	-	6	13	20	27	—
F	4	11	18	25	—	1	8	15	22	29	-	7	14	21	28	—
S	5	12	19	26	—	2	9	16	23	—	1	8	15	22	29	—

	April					May					June				
☉	-	6	13	20	27	-	4	11	18	25	1	8	15	22	29
M	-	7	14	21	28	-	5	12	19	26	2	9	16	23	30
Tu	1	8	15	22	29	-	6	13	20	27	3	10	17	24	—
W	2	9	16	23	30	-	7	14	21	28	4	11	18	25	—
Th	3	10	17	24	—	1	8	15	22	29	5	12	19	26	—
F	4	11	18	25	—	2	9	16	23	30	6	13	20	27	—
S	5	12	19	26	—	3	10	17	24	31	7	14	21	28	—

	July					August					September				
☉	-	6	13	20	27	-	3	10	17	24	31	-	7	14	21	28
M	-	7	14	21	28	-	4	11	18	25	—	1	8	15	22	29
Tu	1	8	15	22	29	-	5	12	19	26	—	2	9	16	23	30
W	2	9	16	23	30	-	6	13	20	27	—	3	10	17	24	—
Th	3	10	17	24	31	-	7	14	21	28	—	4	11	18	25	—
F	4	11	18	25	—	1	8	15	22	29	—	5	12	19	26	—
S	5	12	19	26	—	2	9	16	23	30	—	6	13	20	27	—

	October					November					December				
☉	-	5	12	19	26	-	2	9	16	23	30	-	7	14	21	28
M	-	6	13	20	27	-	3	10	17	24	—	1	8	15	22	29
Tu	-	7	14	21	28	-	4	11	18	25	—	2	9	16	23	30
W	1	8	15	22	29	-	5	12	19	26	—	3	10	17	24	31
Th	2	9	16	23	30	-	6	13	20	27	—	4	11	18	25	—
F	3	10	17	24	31	-	7	14	21	28	—	5	12	19	26	—
S	4	11	18	25	—	1	8	15	22	29	—	6	13	20	27	—

F

7. Common Years in which 1 January falls on a Wednesday

	January						February					March				
S	–	5	12	19	26		–	2	9	16	23		–	2	9	16	23	30
M	–	6	13	20	27		–	3	10	17	24		–	3	10	17	24	31
Tu	–	7	14	21	28		–	4	11	18	25		–	4	11	18	25	–
W	1	8	15	22	29		–	5	12	19	26		–	5	12	19	26	–
Th	2	9	16	23	30		–	6	13	20	27		–	6	13	20	27	–
F	3	10	17	24	31		–	7	14	21	28		–	7	14	21	28	–
S	4	11	18	25	–		1	8	15	22	–		1	8	15	22	29	–

	April						May						June				
S	–	6	13	20	27		–	4	11	18	25		1	8	15	22	29
M	–	7	14	21	28		–	5	12	19	26		2	9	16	23	30
Tu	1	8	15	22	29		–	6	13	20	27		3	10	17	24	–
W	2	9	16	23	30		–	7	14	21	28		4	11	18	25	–
Th	3	10	17	24	–		1	8	15	22	29		5	12	19	26	–
F	4	11	18	25	–		2	9	16	23	30		6	13	20	27	–
S	5	12	19	26	–		3	10	17	24	31		7	14	21	28	–

	July						August						September				
S	–	6	13	20	27		–	3	10	17	24	31		–	7	14	21	28
M	–	7	14	21	28		–	4	11	18	25	–		1	8	15	22	29
Tu	1	8	15	22	29		–	5	12	19	26	–		2	9	16	23	30
W	2	9	16	23	30		–	6	13	20	27	–		3	10	17	24	–
Th	3	10	17	24	31		–	7	14	21	28	–		4	11	18	25	–
F	4	11	18	25	–		1	8	15	22	29	–		5	12	19	26	–
S	5	12	19	26	–		2	9	16	23	30	–		6	13	20	27	–

	October						November						December				
S	–	5	12	19	26		–	2	9	16	23	30		–	7	14	21	28
M	–	6	13	20	27		–	3	10	17	24	–		1	8	15	22	29
Tu	–	7	14	21	28		–	4	11	18	25	–		2	9	16	23	30
W	1	8	15	22	29		–	5	12	19	26	–		3	10	17	24	31
Th	2	9	16	23	30		–	6	13	20	27	–		4	11	18	25	–
F	3	10	17	24	31		–	7	14	21	28	–		5	12	19	26	–
S	4	11	18	25	–		1	8	15	22	29	–		6	13	20	27	–

8. Leap Years in which 1 January falls on a Wednesday

	January	February	March
S	– 5 12 19 26	– 2 9 16 23	1 8 15 22 29
M	– 6 13 20 27	– 3 10 17 24	2 9 16 23 30
Tu	– 7 14 21 28	– 4 11 18 25	3 10 17 24 31
W	1 8 15 22 29	– 5 12 19 26	4 11 18 25 –
Th	2 9 16 23 30	– 6 13 20 27	5 12 19 26 –
F	3 10 17 24 31	– 7 14 21 28	6 13 20 27 –
S	4 11 18 25 –	1 8 15 22 29	7 14 21 28 –

	April	May	June
S	– 5 12 19 26	– 3 10 17 24 31	– 7 14 21 28
M	– 6 13 20 27	– 4 11 18 25 –	1 8 15 22 29
Tu	– 7 14 21 28	– 5 12 19 26 –	2 9 16 23 30
W	1 8 15 22 29	– 6 13 20 27 –	3 10 17 24 –
Th	2 9 16 23 30	– 7 14 21 28 –	4 11 18 25 –
F	3 10 17 24 –	1 8 15 22 29 –	5 12 19 26 –
S	4 11 18 25 –	2 9 16 23 30 –	6 13 20 27 –

	July	August	September
S	– 5 12 19 26	– 2 9 16 23 30	– 6 13 20 27
M	– 6 13 20 27	– 3 10 17 24 31	– 7 14 21 28
Tu	– 7 14 21 28	– 4 11 18 25 –	1 8 15 22 29
W	1 8 15 22 29	– 5 12 19 26 –	2 9 16 23 30
Th	2 9 16 23 30	– 6 13 20 27 –	3 10 17 24 –
F	3 10 17 24 31	– 7 14 21 28 –	4 11 18 25 –
S	4 11 18 25 –	1 8 15 22 29 –	5 12 19 26 –

	October	November	December
S	– 4 11 18 25	1 8 15 22 29	– 6 13 20 27
M	– 5 12 19 26	2 9 16 23 30	– 7 14 21 28
T	– 6 13 20 27	3 10 17 24 –	1 8 15 22 29
W	– 7 14 21 28	4 11 18 25 –	2 9 16 23 30
Th	1 8 15 22 29	5 12 19 26 –	3 10 17 24 31
F	2 9 16 23 30	6 13 20 27 –	4 11 18 25 –
S	3 10 17 24 31	7 14 21 28 –	5 12 19 26 –

9. Common Years in which 1 January falls on a Thursday

		January						February					March			
S	–	4	11	18	25		1	8	15	22		1	8	15	22	29
M	–	5	12	19	26		2	9	16	23		2	9	16	23	30
Tu	–	6	13	20	27		3	10	17	24		3	10	17	24	31
W	–	7	14	21	28		4	11	18	25		4	11	18	25	–
Th	1	8	15	22	29		5	12	19	26		5	12	19	26	–
F	2	9	16	23	30		6	13	20	27		6	13	20	27	–
S	3	10	17	24	31		7	14	21	28		7	14	21	28	–

		April						May						June			
S	–	5	12	19	26		–	3	10	17	24	31	–	7	14	21	28
M	–	6	13	20	27		–	4	11	18	25	–	1	8	15	22	29
Tu	–	7	14	21	28		–	5	12	19	26	–	2	9	16	23	30
W	1	8	15	22	29		–	6	13	20	27	–	3	10	17	24	–
Th	2	9	16	23	30		–	7	14	21	28	–	4	11	18	25	–
F	3	10	17	24	–		1	8	15	22	29	–	5	12	19	26	–
S	4	11	18	25	–		2	9	16	23	30	–	6	13	20	27	–

		July						August						September			
S	–	5	12	19	26		–	2	9	16	23	30	–	6	13	20	27
M	–	6	13	20	27		–	3	10	17	24	31	–	7	14	21	28
Tu	–	7	14	21	28		–	4	11	18	25	–	1	8	15	22	29
W	1	8	15	22	29		–	5	12	19	26	–	2	9	16	23	30
Th	2	9	16	23	30		–	6	13	20	27	–	3	10	17	24	–
F	3	10	17	24	31		–	7	14	21	28	–	4	11	18	25	–
S	4	11	18	25	–		1	8	15	22	29	–	5	12	19	26	–

		October						November						December			
S	–	4	11	18	25		1	8	15	22	29		–	6	13	20	27
M	–	5	12	19	26		2	9	16	23	30		–	7	14	21	28
Tu	–	6	13	20	27		3	10	17	24	–		1	8	15	22	29
W	–	7	14	21	28		4	11	18	25	–		2	9	16	23	30
Th	1	8	15	22	29		5	12	19	26	–		3	10	17	24	31
F	2	9	16	23	30		6	13	20	27	–		4	11	18	25	–
S	3	10	17	24	31		7	14	21	28	–		5	12	19	26	–

10. *Leap Years in which 1 January falls on a Thursday*

	January	February	March
S	– 4 11 18 25	1 8 15 22 29	– 7 14 21 28
M	– 5 12 19 26	2 9 16 23 —	1 8 15 22 29
Tu	– 6 13 20 27	3 10 17 24 —	2 9 16 23 30
W	– 7 14 21 28	4 11 18 25 —	3 10 17 24 31
Th	1 8 15 22 29	5 12 19 26 —	4 11 18 25 —
F	2 9 16 23 30	6 13 20 27 —	5 12 19 26 —
S	3 10 17 24 31	7 14 21 28 —	6 13 20 27 —

	April	May	June
S	– 4 11 18 25	– 2 9 16 23 30	– 6 13 20 27
M	– 5 12 19 26	– 3 10 17 24 31	– 7 14 21 28
Tu	– 6 13 20 27	– 4 11 18 25 —	1 8 15 22 29
W	– 7 14 21 28	– 5 12 19 26 —	2 9 16 23 30
Th	1 8 15 22 29	– 6 13 20 27 —	3 10 17 24 —
F	2 9 16 23 30	– 7 14 21 28 —	4 11 18 25 —
S	3 10 17 24 —	1 8 15 22 29 —	5 12 19 26 —

	July	August	September
S	– 4 11 18 25	1 8 15 22 29	– 5 12 19 26
M	– 5 12 19 26	2 9 16 23 30	– 6 13 20 27
Tu	– 6 13 20 27	3 10 17 24 31	– 7 14 21 28
W	– 7 14 21 28	4 11 18 25 —	1 8 15 22 29
Th	1 8 15 22 29	5 12 19 26 —	2 9 16 23 30
F	2 9 16 23 30	6 13 20 27 —	3 10 17 24 —
S	3 10 17 24 31	7 14 21 28 —	4 11 18 25 —

	October	November	December
S	– 3 10 17 24 31	– 7 14 21 28	– 5 12 19 26
M	– 4 11 18 25 —	1 8 15 22 29	– 6 13 20 27
Tu	– 5 12 19 26 —	2 9 16 23 30	– 7 14 21 28
W	– 6 13 20 27 —	3 10 17 24 —	1 8 15 22 29
Th	– 7 14 21 28 —	4 11 18 25 —	2 9 16 23 30
F	1 8 15 22 29 —	5 12 19 26 —	3 10 17 24 31
S	2 9 16 23 30 —	6 13 20 27 —	4 11 18 25 —

11. *Common Years in which 1 January falls on a Friday*

	January		February		March
S	– 3 10 17 24 31		– 7 14 21 28		– 7 14 21 28
M	– 4 11 18 25 —		1 8 15 22 —		1 8 15 22 29
Tu	– 5 12 19 26 —		2 9 16 23 —		2 9 16 23 30
W	– 6 13 20 27 —		3 10 17 24 —		3 10 17 24 31
Th	– 7 14 21 28 —		4 11 18 25 —		4 11 18 25 —
F	1 8 15 22 29 —		5 12 19 26 —		5 12 19 26 —
S	2 9 16 23 30 —		6 13 20 27 —		6 13 20 27 —

	April		May		June
S	– 4 11 18 25		– 2 9 16 23 30		– 6 13 20 27
M	– 5 12 19 26		– 3 10 17 24 31		– 7 14 21 28
Tu	– 6 13 20 27		– 4 11 18 25 —		1 8 15 22 29
W	– 7 14 21 28		– 5 12 19 26 —		2 9 16 23 30
Th	1 8 15 22 29		– 6 13 20 27 —		3 10 17 24 —
F	2 9 16 23 30		– 7 14 21 28 —		4 11 18 25 —
S	3 10 17 24 —		1 8 15 22 29 —		5 12 19 26 —

	July		August		September
S	– 4 11 18 25		1 8 15 22 29		– 5 12 19 26
M	– 5 12 19 26		2 9 16 23 30		– 6 13 20 27
Tu	– 6 13 20 27		3 10 17 24 31		– 7 14 21 28
W	– 7 14 21 28		4 11 18 25 —		1 8 15 22 29
Th	1 8 15 22 29		5 12 19 26 —		2 9 16 23 30
F	2 9 16 23 30		6 13 20 27 —		3 10 17 24 —
S	3 10 17 24 31		7 14 21 28 —		4 11 18 25 —

	October		November		December
S	– 3 10 17 24 31		– 7 14 21 28		– 5 12 19 26
M	– 4 11 18 25 —		1 8 15 22 29		– 6 13 20 27
Tu	– 5 12 19 26 —		2 9 16 23 30		– 7 14 21 28
W	– 6 13 20 27 —		3 10 17 24 —		1 8 15 22 29
Th	– 7 14 21 28 —		4 11 18 25 —		2 9 16 23 30
F	1 8 15 22 29 —		5 12 19 26 —		3 10 17 24 31
S	2 9 16 23 30 —		6 13 20 27 —		4 11 18 25 —

12. Leap Years in which 1 January falls on a Friday

	January	February	March
S	– 3 10 17 24 31	– 7 14 21 28	– 6 13 20 27
M	– 4 11 18 25 –	1 8 15 22 29	– 7 14 21 28
Tu	– 5 12 19 26 –	2 9 16 23 –	1 8 15 22 29
W	– 6 13 20 27 –	3 10 17 24 –	2 9 16 23 30
Th	– 7 14 21 28 –	4 11 18 25 –	3 10 17 24 31
F	1 8 15 22 29 –	5 12 19 26 –	4 11 18 25 –
S	2 9 16 23 30 –	6 13 20 27 –	5 12 19 26 –

	April	May	June
S	– 3 10 17 24	1 8 15 22 29	– 5 12 19 26
M	– 4 11 18 25	2 9 16 23 30	– 6 13 20 27
Tu	– 5 12 19 26	3 10 17 24 31	– 7 14 21 28
W	– 6 13 20 27	4 11 18 25 –	1 8 15 22 29
Th	– 7 14 21 28	5 12 19 26 –	2 9 16 23 30
F	1 8 15 22 29	6 13 20 27 –	3 10 17 24 –
S	2 9 16 23 30	7 14 21 28 –	4 11 18 25 –

	July	August	September
S	– 3 10 17 24 31	– 7 14 21 28	– 4 11 18 25
M	– 4 11 18 25 –	1 8 15 22 29	– 5 12 19 26
Tu	– 5 12 19 26 –	2 9 16 23 30	– 6 13 20 27
W	– 6 13 20 27 –	3 10 17 24 31	– 7 14 21 28
Th	– 7 14 21 28 –	4 11 18 25 –	1 8 15 22 29
F	1 8 15 22 29 –	5 12 19 26 –	2 9 16 23 30
S	2 9 16 23 30 –	6 13 20 27 –	3 10 17 24 –

	October	November	December
S	– 2 9 16 23 30	– 6 13 20 27	– 4 11 18 25
M	– 3 10 17 24 31	– 7 14 21 28	– 5 12 19 26
Tu	– 4 11 18 25 –	1 8 15 22 29	– 6 13 20 27
W	– 5 12 19 26 –	2 9 16 23 30	– 7 14 21 28
Th	– 6 13 20 27 –	3 10 17 24 –	1 8 15 22 29
F	– 7 14 21 28 –	4 11 18 25 –	2 9 16 23 30
S	1 8 15 22 29 –	5 12 19 26 –	3 10 17 24 31

13. Common Years in which 1 January falls on a Saturday

	January							February							March					
Su	–	2	9	16	23	30	Su	–	6	13	20	27		Su	–	6	13	20	27	
M	–	3	10	17	24	31	M	–	7	14	21	28		M	–	7	14	21	28	
Tu	–	4	11	18	25	–	Tu	1	8	15	22	–		Tu	1	8	15	22	29	
W	–	5	12	19	26	–	W	2	9	16	23	–		W	2	9	16	23	30	
Th	–	6	13	20	27	–	Th	3	10	17	24	–		Th	3	10	17	24	31	
F	–	7	14	21	28	–	F	4	11	18	25	–		F	4	11	18	25	–	
S	1	8	15	22	29	–	S	5	12	19	26	–		S	5	12	19	26	–	

	April						May						June				
Su	–	3	10	17	24	Su	1	8	15	22	29	Su	–	5	12	19	26
M	–	4	11	18	25	M	2	9	16	23	30	M	–	6	13	20	27
Tu	–	5	12	19	26	Tu	3	10	17	24	31	Tu	–	7	14	21	28
W	–	6	13	20	27	W	4	11	18	25	–	W	1	8	15	22	29
Th	–	7	14	21	28	Th	5	12	19	26	–	Th	2	9	16	23	30
F	1	8	15	22	29	F	6	13	20	27	–	F	3	10	17	24	–
S	2	9	16	23	30	S	7	14	21	28	–	S	4	11	18	25	–

	July						August						September				
Su	–	3	10	17	24	31	–	7	14	21	28		–	4	11	18	25
M	–	4	11	18	25	–	1	8	15	22	29		–	5	12	19	26
Tu	–	5	12	19	26	–	2	9	16	23	30		–	6	13	20	27
W	–	6	13	20	27	–	3	10	17	24	31		–	7	14	21	28
Th	–	7	14	21	28	–	4	11	18	25	–		1	8	15	22	29
F	1	8	15	22	29	–	5	12	19	26	–		2	9	16	23	30
S	2	9	16	23	30	–	6	13	20	27	–		3	10	17	24	–

	October						November					December				
Su	–	2	9	16	23	30	–	6	13	20	27	–	4	11	18	25
M	–	3	10	17	24	31	–	7	14	21	28	–	5	12	19	26
Tu	–	4	11	18	25	–	1	8	15	22	29	–	6	13	20	27
W	–	5	12	19	26	–	2	9	16	23	30	–	7	14	21	28
Th	–	6	13	20	27	–	3	10	17	24	–	1	8	15	22	29
F	–	7	14	21	28	–	4	11	18	25	–	2	9	16	23	30
S	1	8	15	22	29	–	5	12	19	26	–	3	10	17	24	31

14. Leap Years in which 1 January falls on a Saturday

	January							February						March				
S	–	2	9	16	23	30		–	6	13	20	27		–	5	12	19	26
M	–	3	10	17	24	31		–	7	14	21	28		–	6	13	20	27
Tu	–	4	11	18	25	–		1	8	15	22	29		–	7	14	21	28
W	–	5	12	19	26	–		2	9	16	23	–		1	8	15	22	29
Th	–	6	13	20	27	–		3	10	17	24	–		2	9	16	23	30
F	–	7	14	21	28	–		4	11	18	25	–		3	10	17	24	31
S	1	8	15	22	29	–		5	12	19	26	–		4	11	18	25	–

	April							May						June				
S	–	2	9	16	23	30		–	7	14	21	28		–	4	11	18	25
M	–	3	10	17	24	–		1	8	15	22	29		–	5	12	19	26
Tu	–	4	11	18	25	–		2	9	16	23	30		–	6	13	20	27
W	–	5	12	19	26	–		3	10	17	24	31		–	7	14	21	28
Th	–	6	13	20	27	–		4	11	18	25	–		1	8	15	22	29
F	–	7	14	21	28	–		5	12	19	26	–		2	9	16	23	30
S	1	8	15	22	29	–		6	13	20	27	–		3	10	17	24	–

	July							August						September				
S	–	2	9	16	23	30		–	6	13	20	27		–	3	10	17	24
M	–	3	10	17	24	31		–	7	14	21	28		–	4	11	18	25
Tu	–	4	11	18	25	–		1	8	15	22	29		–	5	12	19	26
W	–	5	12	19	26	–		2	9	16	23	30		–	6	13	20	27
Th	–	6	13	20	27	–		3	10	17	24	31		–	7	14	21	28
F	–	7	14	21	28	–		4	11	18	25	–		1	8	15	22	29
S	1	8	15	22	29	–		5	12	19	26	–		2	9	16	23	30

	October							November						December				
S	1	8	15	22	29			–	5	12	19	26		–	3	10	17	24	31
M	2	9	16	23	30			–	6	13	20	27		–	4	11	18	25	–
Tu	3	10	17	24	31			–	7	14	21	28		–	5	12	19	26	–
W	4	11	18	25	–			1	8	15	22	29		–	6	13	20	27	–
Th	5	12	19	26	–			2	9	16	23	30		–	7	14	21	28	–
F	6	13	20	27	–			3	10	17	24	–		1	8	15	22	29	–
S	7	14	21	28	–			4	11	18	25	–		2	9	16	23	30	–

TABLE FIVE: Calendar for October to December, A.D. 1582

The first nine months of the Christian Year 1582 follow the table or Common Years in which 1 January falls on a Saturday, as shown in Table Four, 13, with the Days of the Year as shown in Table Three. A special table is required, therefore, only for October, November and December, as follows.

OCTOBER			NOVEMBER			DECEMBER		
Day of the			Day of the			Day of the		
Year	Month	Week	Year	Month	Week	Year	Month	Week
274	1	S	295	1	S	325	1	M
275	2	Su	296	2	Su	326	2	Tu
276	3	M	297	3	M	327	3	W
277	4	Tu	298	4	Tu	328	4	Th
			299	5	W	329	5	F
NEW STYLE			300	6	Th	330	6	S
278	15	W	301	7	F	331	7	Su
279	16	Th	302	8	S	332	8	M
280	17	F	303	9	Su	333	9	Tu
281	18	S	304	10	M	334	10	W
282	19	Su	305	11	Tu	335	11	Th
283	20	M	306	12	W	336	12	F
284	21	Tu	307	13	Th	337	13	S
285	22	W	308	14	F	338	14	Su
286	23	Th	309	15	S	339	15	M
287	24	F	310	16	Su	340	16	Tu
288	25	S	311	17	M	341	17	W
289	26	Su	312	18	Tu	342	18	Th
290	27	M	313	19	W	343	19	F
291	28	Tu	314	20	Th	344	20	S
292	29	W	315	21	F	345	21	Su
293	30	Th	316	22	S	346	22	M
294	31	F	317	23	Su	347	23	Tu
			318	24	M	348	24	W
			319	25	Tu	349	25	Th
			320	26	W	350	26	F
			321	27	Th	351	27	S
			322	28	F	352	28	Su
			323	29	S	353	29	M
			324	30	Su	354	30	Tu
						355	31	W

TABLE SIX: **The Principal Muslim Festivals**

(Festivals peculiar to the Shi'a are indicated by an asterisk)

1 Muharram:	New Year's Day.
10 Muharram:	Commemoration of the Battle of Karbala.
*16 Muharram:	Imamat Day (Ismaili Khoja only).
12 Rabi' al-Awal:	Mulid al-Nabi (Birth of the Prophet Muhammad).
*23 Jumada al-Ukhra:	Birth of Agha Khan IV (Ismaili only).
27 Rajab:	Lailat al-Miraj (ascent of the Prophet Muhammad into Heaven).
1 Ramadhan:	The beginning of the month of fasting.
21 Ramadhan:	Lailat al-Qadr ('The Night of Power').
1 Shawwal:	'Id al-Fitr. (The celebration of this festival commonly continues for from two to three days.)
10 Dhu al-Hijja:	'Id al-Hajj. (This festival commonly continues for at least two days.)

TABLE SEVEN: The Principal Fixed Christian Festivals

1 January:	The Circumcision of Christ, New Year's Day.
25 March:	The Annunciation of the Blessed Virgin Mary.
15 August:	The Assumption of the Blessed Virgin Mary.
1 November:	All Saints' Day.
2 November:	All Souls' Day.
25 December:	Christmas Day.

TABLE EIGHT: **Movable Christian Festivals**

Year	Septuagesima	Ash Wednesday	Easter	Ascension	Whit Sunday	Corpus Christi	First Sunday of Advent
1960	14 Feb.	2 March	17 April	26 May	5 June	16 June	27 Nov.
1961	29 Jan.	15 Feb.	2 April	11 May	21 May	1 June	3 Dec.
1962	18 Feb.	7 March	22 April	31 May	10 June	21 June	2 Dec.
1963	10 Feb.	27 Feb.	14 April	23 May	2 June	13 June	1 Dec.
1964	26 Jan.	12 Feb.	29 March	7 May	17 May	28 May	29 Nov.
1965	14 Feb.	3 March	18 April	27 May	6 June	17 June	28 Nov.
1966	6 Feb.	23 Feb.	10 April	19 May	29 May	9 June	27 Nov.
1967	22 Jan.	8 Feb.	26 March	4 May	14 May	25 May	3 Dec.
1968	11 Feb.	28 Feb.	14 April	23 May	2 June	13 June	1 Dec.
1969	2 Feb.	19 Feb.	6 April	15 May	25 May	5 June	30 Nov.
1970	25 Jan.	11 Feb.	29 March	7 May	17 May	28 May	29 Nov.
1971	7 Feb.	24 Feb.	11 April	20 May	30 May	10 June	28 Nov.
1972	30 Jan.	16 Feb.	2 April	11 May	21 May	1 June	3 Dec.
1973	18 Feb.	7 March	22 April	31 May	10 June	21 June	2 Dec.
1974	10 Feb.	27 Feb.	14 April	23 May	2 June	13 June	1 Dec.

Year	Septuagesima	Ash Wednesday	Easter	Ascension	Whit Sunday	Corpus Christi	First Sunday of Advent
1975	26 Jan.	12 Feb.	30 March	8 May	18 May	29 May	30 Nov.
1976	15 Feb.	3 March	18 April	27 May	6 June	17 June	28 Nov.
1977	6 Feb.	23 Feb.	10 April	19 May	29 May	9 June	27 Nov.
1978	22 Jan.	8 Feb.	26 March	4 May	14 May	25 May	3 Dec.
1979	11 Feb.	28 Feb.	15 April	24 May	3 June	14 June	2 Dec.
1980	3 Feb.	20 Feb.	6 April	15 May	25 May	5 June	30 Nov.
1981	15 Feb.	4 March	19 April	28 May	7 June	18 June	29 Nov.
1982	7 Feb.	24 Feb.	11 April	20 May	30 May	10 June	28 Nov.
1983	30 Jan.	16 Feb.	3 April	12 May	22 May	2 June	27 Nov.
1984	19 Feb.	7 March	22 April	31 May	10 June	21 June	2 Dec.
1985	3 Feb.	20 Feb.	7 April	16 May	26 May	6 June	1 Dec.
1986	26 Jan.	12 Feb.	30 March	8 May	18 May	29 May	30 Nov.
1987	15 Feb.	4 March	19 April	28 May	7 June	18 June	29 Nov.
1988	31 Jan.	17 Feb.	3 April	12 May	22 May	2 June	27 Nov.
1989	22 Jan.	8 Feb.	26 March	4 May	14 May	25 May	3 Dec.
1990	11 Feb.	28 Feb.	15 April	24 May	3 June	14 June	2 Dec.